John Hancock

New England Boy

Illustrated by Gray Morrow

John Hancock

New England Boy

By Cathrine Seward Cleven

jB
H 1912 c

THE **BOBBS-MERRILL** COMPANY, INC.
A SUBSIDIARY OF HOWARD W. SAMS & CO., INC.
Publishers • INDIANAPOLIS • NEW YORK

To my granddaughter
Lori Kay

The author wishes to thank Mr. H. Hobart Holly, President of the Quincy, Massachusetts, Historical Society, for his interest and aid.

Illustrations

Numerous smaller illustrations

Contents

CHILDHOOD
OF FAMOUS
AMERICANS

®

John Hancock

New England Boy

Johnny Meets
Little Turtle

JOHNNY HANCOCK knelt under the lilac bush. He peeked out at the black dragon coming toward him. Then he looked at his sister Mary's wooden doll. She lay with her painted face in the dirt.

"Fear not, fair one," he said. "Saint George will save you."

He lifted his long stick. A cold drop of rain from the lilac leaves ran down his cheek.

The black dragon snorted and came closer to the garden.

The lilac bush stood behind Parson John Hancock's square white house in Braintree, in the royal colony of Massachusetts. Hancocks had lived near Boston Town, Massachusetts, for a hundred years. Now it was the summer of 1742.

The black dragon was old Dame Clark's black pig, Daisy. Daisy was always getting loose and running away. Then she would dig up the neighbors' gardens.

"You'll not dig up our garden," five-year-old Johnny shouted. He ran toward the black pig, shaking his stick.

Daisy squealed, "Oink, oink," but she did not run away. Instead, she ran right at Johnny! Before he could say "scat!" she dodged his stick and ran between his legs.

Johnny felt himself being lifted up. Suddenly he was riding on Daisy's back, bumpety-bump! He started to slide off because her back was slippery. He grabbed for her curly tail.

Then he bounced off and rolled over and over into a puddle left from the rain. Daisy ran squealing around the house. Someone else would

have to catch her! Suddenly Johnny heard someone laughing behind him.

"Ho, ho! Ha, ha!"

Then his friend John Adams came running up.
John, who was past six, was short and sturdy.
Johnny called him "Jay."

"That looked so funny," Jay said with a grin.
He put down the basket he carried.

Johnny scrambled to his feet. The back of his
dress was wet. Johnny had to wear a dress until
he went to school, just as all small boys did.

"Let's see," Jay Adams said. He pulled Johnny
around. "You will catch it."

"I will not," Johnny said. "I have lots of
clothes." His dark eyes flashed, but he and his
friend both knew that a parson's son didn't have
many clothes.

Johnny looked curiously at Jay's basket.
"What's in here?" he asked. He lifted the lid.
Inside he saw a pile of shelled Indian corn.

13

Jay smiled proudly. "This is Dame Belcher's corn. You know, my teacher at Dame School."

Johnny nodded and waited.

"She asked me to take her corn to the grist mill," Jay went on. "She likes her corn ground into corn meal fresh every day. She says it makes her corn-and-rye bread and johnnycake taste better."

"Are you going to do this every day after school, Jay?"

"Maybe, Johnny. She's going to give me three coppers," Jay added proudly.

"Three coppers!" Johnny's eyes grew wider. He never had had so much money.

"I wish I could go to Dame School," he said. "I want to learn to read and write my name. I can say my ABC's. Father taught me."

"You can go after New Year's Day," Jay said. "You'll be six in January, when I'll be seven."

Johnny shook his head sadly. "You won't be

14

there. You'll go to the Free Latin School by Father's Meeting House."

"Maybe I'll stay at Dame Belcher's another year. I like her. She teaches us to cipher—that means to add numbers. That isn't taught in Latin School until we're much older. If I stay I can earn more coppers, too," Jay added wisely.

"Johnny! Johnny Hancock!" Seven-year-old Mary Hancock stepped out of the kitchen door. There was a smear of corn meal on her cheek. She had been helping Mother in the big kitchen.

"What have you done to your nice dress? Oh, Mother-r-r!" she called.

"Aw-w-w, I fell. The dragon knocked me over. Must you tell Mother?"

Mary frowned and gave him a gentle shove toward the kitchen door. Then she remembered her manners. "Will you come, too, Jay?"

"No, thank you, Mary," Jay said. "I have to go to the mill and then back home. I stopped to tell

Johnny I can go fishing with him tomorrow. There's no school."

The Adams family lived on a farm at the foot of Penn's Hill. It was about a mile down the Coast Road which wound along Boston Bay. From the top of Penn's Hill one could see ten miles across Boston Bay to Boston Town itself.

Jay Adams picked up his basket of corn. He ran around the house to the road. A moment later Johnny and Mary heard him whooping and yelling as he ran along.

Johnny followed his sister slowly into the kitchen. Mother glanced up from the fireplace. Her face looked warm under her frilled white cap. "Who is that whooping outside?"she cried.

"Oh, that's just Jay Adams chasing the dragon." Johnny laughed.

"Foolish boy!" Mary turned Johnny around so that Mother could see his back. "He's all wet."

Mother stood up. She smoothed down the

16

blue apron she wore over her blue and white striped skirt. "Maybe I should let you wash your own linen. Then you might learn to stay clean."

"Yes, Mother."

"Go to your room and find a fresh dress," she said. "I am much too busy. A neighbor just brought me word from Boston Town. Your Uncle Thomas Hancock and Aunt Lydia are coming here to visit tomorrow."

"Uncle Tom!" Johnny clapped his hands. "Now I can ride in the carriage!"

Mother smiled. "You're as noisy as the Indian children camped out at Colonel John Quincy's farm. Go along with you."

"Mother," Mary said, "I think Johnny likes fine things too well. Doesn't Father say that is a sin?"

"That's what the old Puritans believed. But people are earning more than in the old days. There are more good things to share."

"Uncle Thomas has a fine house in Boston. He must have——" Mary began.

Mother frowned. "Yes, your father's brother is very rich. He is a merchant and a trader with England. He has worked very hard. It is too bad he has no children."

Baby Ebenezer set up a cry. He was learning to walk and had just taken a tumble in a corner of the kitchen.

"Oh, dear," said Mother. "Will you quiet him, Mary? Your father is working on his two Sunday sermons, and I must get my bread baked. If I'd only known Thomas and Lydia were coming I might have sent to Boston for wheat flour."

Johnny ran out of the room. When he came back in dry clothes he asked Mother, "When will they get here? I can't wait."

"I'll tell you about it at supper, son. We shall eat as soon as Father finishes his sermons. Now run along and don't bother me."

18

Johnny gave a sigh. "That will be a long time," he said. He went out to the barn to pet Father's horse, Betsy.

He was eating breakfast early the next morning when he heard Jay Adams' whistle outside. The family ate often in the big kitchen, which was a room added on to the back of the house.

Johnny looked at Father.

"Wait until we say the prayer, John." Father smiled kindly at him.

Johnny had often heard people say that Parson Hancock was wise, kind, and a very good speaker. He knew that people came from far away to hear him preach.

When Johnny at last ran to the door, he saw his friend Jay waiting with a fishing pole over his shoulder.

"Good morrow to you," Johnny said. "Do you have a pole for me?"

"No, I'll cut you one from a young tree with

19

my pocketknife," Jay told him. "I have a fish hook for you, though."

Mother went to the door. "Watch him well, Jay. Stay on the bridge to fish. I don't want him falling into the creek."

"Yes, ma'am."

"And be back for dinner this noon, Johnny. Today is Saturday. Your uncle and aunt will come this afternoon. Good-by, boys."

"Catch me a fish," Mary called after them. But the boys were already busy talking about their fishing plans.

Johnny tried hard to keep up with Jay Adams' trot. They went up the dusty highway past a few scattered houses and some orchards to Black Creek. The creek flowed into Boston Bay.

When the boys reached the log bridge that crossed the creek, they were warm from the August sun. Jay put one of the worms he had brought with him on his hook. He gave his pole to Johnny to hold. Johnny dropped the hook and line into the water.

Then Jay found a long green stick on the creek bank and cut it with his knife. He tied a line and hook to it for Johnny.

The two boys fished and fished, but they didn't get a bite.

The sun rose higher in the sky. By and by some dark clouds began to gather around it.

"If I could just get one fish for my uncle and aunt," Johnny thought. "Everyone eats fish on Saturdays. And I'll have to go home soon."

Just then he looked up. He saw a head peek out from behind a tree. It was a boy with bright black eyes and long black hair.

Johnny gave Jay's foot a little kick. "Look!"

Jay's round face broke into a smile.

"Well! It's Little Turtle. He's one of the Ponkhapoag Indians. They're camping at Colonel Quincy's farm near the bay. They're made to live on a place at Stoughton, but they come here each year for the fishing. They're always hungry."

Now the Indian boy was standing at the end of the bridge. "Fish?" he asked. "How many?"

Jay made a face. "Not one, Little Turtle."

Little Turtle edged closer. "Me catch."

"Go ahead."

"Get fish—you give hook?"

"Yes," Johnny whispered eagerly to Jay. "Give him my hook."

Jay nodded. "Show us, Little Turtle."

A Fish and Some Eggs

LITTLE TURTLE rubbed his bare toes over the logs of the bridge. A slow smile spread across his face.

He pointed to a shiny blue dragonfly that had lighted on the rushing water. Swish! Bubbles marked the spot where the dragonfly had been. A fish had snapped it up!

"Eat flies, grasshoppers today," Little Turtle said. He moved his dirty brown hands like wings. "No worms."

"Grasshoppers! We'll catch some!" Johnny and Jay cried in the same breath.

Together the three boys roamed the creek

banks. The sun went under a cloud, and there came the rumble of summer thunder.

Soon each boy had a grasshopper in his closed fist. Little Turtle put a grasshopper on Johnny's hook and handed the pole to Johnny. Jay put one on his hook.

Johnny's grasshopper had floated downstream only a moment or two when Johnny felt a sudden tug. The grasshopper disappeared, and the pole pulled at Johnny's hand as if it were alive.

"I got one!" he shouted. "What'll I do?"

"Hang on!" Jay shouted. "I have one, too."

Johnny pulled and pulled. He would *never* let this one get away. But would his green stick hold? It did not look strong.

Little Turtle put his hands on the stick. Together he and Johnny gave a great jerk. The fish flew out of the creek, hit Jay on the head, and dropped to the bridge.

Jay flipped his fish out of the water, too. Then he glared at Johnny. "Why did you hit me with your fish?"

"Oh, never mind!" Johnny said excitedly. "You didn't hurt it any. Oh, did you ever see such a big one?" He dragged his gasping prize over beside Jay's fish.

"Mine's larger," Jay declared after measuring the two fish carefully. "But yours is good for your first fish."

Suddenly rain started to fall. "Oh, we've got

to go!" Jay said. "Under those trees until it stops raining."

"Tree no good in bad storm," Little Turtle spoke up. "Lightning hit. Come. Go wigwam."

Jay grabbed Johnny's hand. "Let's go," he said. "Hurry!"

They followed the Indian boy along the creek bank. Johnny's short legs had trouble keeping up with the older boys. His bare feet slipped on a muddy spot, and he fell to his knees. He brushed the rain out of his eyes.

He was glad, indeed, to crowd into Little Turtle's wigwam. It was placed with several others among some pine trees. On one side of the trees was a fenced grain field belonging to the Quincy farm. Fish nets were spread over low bushes near by. The fish that had been spread out to dry on trays and sticks were now covered with pieces of old canvas.

Inside the wigwam it was dark and smoky. An

26

opening at the top let out the smoke from the tiny cook fire. A wet, thin dog smelling of fish steamed close to the fire.

Little Turtle's father, White Bear, sat cross-legged on the dirt floor. People gave him the English name of Moses and called him "King" because he was the last head of the small tribe.

Now he was bending his stern, sad face over a long piece of wood, working on it with a knife. Back of him an Indian woman in old clothes patted corn meal and water into cakes.

Little Turtle spoke to his family in strange words. Then White Bear spoke. "Welcome to our wigwam, young braves."

"Thank you," the boys murmured and sat down on the ground.

Little Turtle's mother brought blackberries in a polished bowl made from a knot of maple wood. Johnny knew his mother prized one like it very highly.

27

Johnny stuffed the berries in his mouth. M-m-m, they were good!

White Bear spoke again. "We come here to catch fish and dry them. In winter we have only dried fish to eat. Now the Quincy family shares its fruit and cider with us. We share with you."

Johnny was sorry he had eaten the food. He sat and listened to the rain outside. Dogs and children were noisy in the next wigwam.

Suddenly Johnny saw what "King Moses" was making—a broom! He watched closely as the Indian carefully shaved the wide end of his piece of birch into long fine strips. This would be the brush end. The other end had already been cut down into a long smooth handle.

No wonder these Indians were poor! Everybody—boys, peddlers, squaws, and girls—made and sold brooms.

Johnny felt hot and sticky in his damp clothes. He wanted to go home with his prize. He patted the dead fish, which was still fastened to the hook and line.

"Here's the hook we promised you," he said suddenly. He handed the fish over to Little Turtle, who easily took out the hook.

The rain stopped. Little Turtle went outside. In a moment he was back with a handful of long wet grass from the creek bank. He wrapped it around Johnny's fish and handed it back to him with a shy smile. Then he did the same for Jay.

Johnny and Jay looked outside. Sunlight danced through the wet pine branches and across the golden grain fields stretching down to the sea. The air grew hot again.

"Good-by and thanks!" Jay said to their Indian friends.

Johnny said, "I'll bring you some eggs."

As they ran back to the main road, the long grass whipped water over their bare legs.

When Johnny entered the lean-to kitchen at

home, he heard a fish peddler's horn sounding down the road.

Sister Mary spied his fish. "Oh, you really caught one! See, Mother, isn't it fine?"

Mother already was broiling several of the peddler's fat codfish in a long-handled iron frying pan.

"Where have you been, Johnny? We were worried during the shower. I see you're muddy again."

"But look at my fish! Mother, I prom——"

"Aye, you've done well." She patted his head. "Give it to me and I shall clean it outside. Mary, hold the pan over the fire. Mind, don't burn your fingers."

She stopped at the door. "Change to a clean dress, Johnny, and put on your shoes. You know Uncle Thomas and Aunt Lydia are coming."

Uncle Thomas! Johnny stood still. He had forgotten in his excitement over the fish. This afternoon he might have a ride in a real carriage. That would be more fun than riding behind Father on Betsy!

He was the first one of the family to see the open carriage with two horses as it pulled up before the gate. In it sat stout Uncle Thomas in his large powdered wig. Across from him spread Aunt Lydia, a mountain of a woman.

Prince, the coachman, jumped down. He and Uncle Thomas helped Aunt Lydia unfold from the carriage and step down to the ground.

Aunt Lydia's eyes were black and shiny as beetles. She had stern eyebrows. But Johnny was not afraid of her. He knew she loved him.

She and Uncle Tom were greeted warmly by the whole family. Uncle Tom, who looked splendid in blue silk and gold lace, lifted Johnny high in the air. He rode him on his broad shoulder into the house.

"Heh, heh!" he chuckled. "What a fine lad!

Could be a mite heavier, though. Just come to Boston to visit us, my boy, and we'll fatten you up."

Mother took them into the cool parlor. Here were her best silver candlesticks and chairs with seats of red velvet.

Aunt Lydia's chair squeaked when she let herself down into it. She and her wide skirts of soft Chinese cotton hid all the chair. Johnny thought she looked as if she were sitting on nothing at all!

"Yes, indeed," she was saying. "We've come to hear one of your sermons tomorrow, Pastor John. See that it's a good one."

"I do my best, Lydia." Father smiled, not minding a bit. "And how is your shipping business in Boston Town, Tom?" He turned to his younger brother.

"Business is fine!" Uncle Tom replied with a chuckle. "But only because I was smart enough to lay in a large supply of whale oil before this war started in Europe. There's a big market for whale oil in England."

Then he frowned. "If only England would let us trade wherever we wanted to, instead of only with her. 'Tis not fair. But we have ways of getting around that sometimes."

Parson Hancock said, "We must guard our rights as free Englishmen, Thomas. Our royal Massachusetts charter gives us great freedom— more than we had in England. And we must keep it so."

Johnny didn't know what all this meant. But he knew better than to speak when grown-ups were talking.

He tugged at Uncle Tom's arm. At last his uncle looked down at him with a smile. "Eh?"

"If you please, sir——" Johnny waved his hand toward the window. The carriage horses were still standing outside, tied to the hitching post in front of the house.

33

"Ah, you remember I promised you a ride the last time I came, do you? A ride you shall have, just as soon as the horses are rested a bit. They pulled quite a load from Boston Town." He laughed, and Aunt Lydia frowned.

Later, when Johnny, Mary, and Uncle Tom were going out the door, Johnny suddenly stopped. He didn't know what to say.

"My promise!" he thought. "I told the Indians I'd bring them eggs and I forgot!"

There was nothing for him to do but find some eggs and carry them out to Little Turtle's camp. He must give up his ride in Uncle Tom's wonderful carriage.

"I can't go," he said fiercely. He ran back to Mother and whispered in her ear. "May I borrow eggs to give to the poor Indians out at the Quincy farm? They gave me fruit when they took me in from the rain. I promised."

Mother looked surprised. "But, Johnny, I

thought you stayed at the Quincy's house when it rained." She smiled down at him with a shake of her head. "What shall I do with you, Johnny Hancock? You're like all the Hancocks, always giving. Yes, take that small basket of eggs out of the pantry. A neighbor brought us an extra dozen this morning."

Besides the money Braintree paid Parson Hancock, the villagers often brought the family food. "Country pay," it was called.

"Thank you, Mother," Johnny said. He got the eggs. Then Uncle Tom popped his head into the kitchen to see what Johnny was doing.

"So you want to walk way out to the Indian camp instead of riding with me, heh?"

"I—I want to go, Uncle, but I promised, and —and—you said you would drive south on the road to Plymouth."

"You're a good boy, Johnny," Uncle Tom said. "I think Prince can turn the horses around the

35

other way. We can drive out to the camp to deliver your eggs."

And so they did. Even White Bear smiled when Uncle Tom gave him a few coins to buy a shirt and shoes for Little Turtle.

Johnny laughed out loud. As if Little Turtle would ever wear shoes!

Up to Boston Town

A COLD March wind whistled around Johnny's knit cap. He clutched his father's black cloak tightly as they rode along through the snow on Betsy, the family horse.

They came to a small schoolhouse sitting under a big tree. "Whoa, Betsy," Father said.

"Thank you, Father!" Johnny slipped down from the horse. "That was better than walking over a mile through the snowdrifts."

"You'll have to walk home at four o'clock, Johnny. I have a long ride to visit sick folk and make calls. I'll not come back this way."

"Yes, sir." Johnny looked down the road at

the Adams farmhouse. He saw no sign of Jay. It was not yet eight o'clock, the time when Dame School started on winter mornings.

X Inside, the school room was cold. Several of the older boys were trying to build up a roaring fire. Their breaths steamed in the cold air.

Dame Belcher, the teacher, sat holding her fingers to the fire. A piece of sewing lay in her lap. She looked like a plump brown hen with a big white cap tied under its chin.

Johnny kept on his coat and mittens. He bowed to Dame Belcher and said, "Good morrow, Mistress." Then he sat down on a form, a plank or wooden bench.

He took off the hornbook that hung around his neck. This hornbook was a piece of wood shaped like a paddle. It was covered with a piece of paper about three by four inches square. The letters of the alphabet, a verse, and the Lord's Prayer were printed on it. Over all was

a thin sheet of horn, through which he could read the letters. All children learned their letters from the horn book.

Sister Mary had given Johnny hers. Now that she was eight, she would no longer come to Dame School. Father would teach her at home.

Johnny opened the copybook he had made by folding sheets of large brown foolscap paper together. He took out his lead plummet, the small stick of lead which he used to write. He began to print his name carefully in his copybook.

School was still new to him, for he had just been going since his sixth birthday in January. After the morning prayer, Dame Belcher asked Jay Adams to pass out fresh goose quills. She mixed ink powder and water for the inkpots.

Johnny scratched out his name on the paper with his quill pen. How he wished the ink wouldn't spatter so! "But you can really tell what the letters are," he thought.

He showed his copybook to Will Salter, who sat next to him. Will looked and snickered.

"What's wrong? Can't you read it?" Johnny whispered crossly.

Will put his hand over his mouth and laughed. "Just about. The letters are crooked and there's a blot——"

"Will Salter!" Dame Belcher stood before the boys. She gave Will a sharp rap on the head with her thimble. "Put on the dunce cap and stand in the corner for laughing and whispering."

Will hung his head and slowly went to the corner of the room.

"You will be there, too, John Hancock, if you whisper more." She looked at his copybook. "Humph! A parson's son must do better. Keep working, young man."

"Yes, mistress," Johnny said, his face hot. Some day he would show her he could write his name well!

He looked back to where Jay Adams sat with the older boys. They were reading their New England primers. Jay grinned and winked.

Johnny forgot his troubles with writing when he finally reached home at dusk. The race home from school and a rousing snowball attack on Daisy, the roaming black pig, had warmed him in the chill air.

He burst into the kitchen. "I'm home!" he called out. The good smell of an Indian pudding of corn meal and molasses cooking made him hungry. The pudding was boiling in a copper kettle that hung from a pothook over the fire in the big fireplace.

Father rested with his boots off before the blazing fire. He was reading a letter aloud to Mother. She held two-year-old Ebenezer in her lap. Mary was knitting a long wool stocking.

Mother looked up and smiled. "Welcome, son. A letter for Father was waiting at the tavern.

It's from Uncle Tom. His gout, his sore foot, still keeps him from paying us a visit."

"Oh, I'm sorry!" Johnny was disappointed.

"He says the road will soon be cleared by the farmers' ox teams. The weather is sure to turn better. He wants us to come in to Boston."

"Huzzah!" Johnny shouted and jumped for joy.

Father shook his head. "Little Ebenezer's cough is bad, and I feel unwell tonight, son. We must put it off."

"It's only ten miles or so, Father," Mary dared to say.

Johnny held his breath. Father looked stern and said, "Mary! We shall wait."

A month later Johnny and Mary rode through Boston's arched brick gates on Boston Neck. The town was almost surrounded by water. A mile of narrow mudflats, called the Neck, tied it to the mainland.

On one side Johnny looked out over wide Boston Harbor, spotted with islands and the Castle Island Fort. On the other side he saw the Charles River flowing down to the harbor.

Uncle Tom's carriage rolled up Cornhill Street. Now the houses stood close together. The horses' hoofs struck the cobblestones sharply as the carriage passed rattling carts and people hurrying to and fro.

This was not Johnny's first visit to the great Hancock house on Beacon Hill. But he did not remember the house clearly from earlier visits.

"Isn't it exciting to travel alone, John?" Mary laughed and squeezed his hand. Father still was not well, and Mother wouldn't leave him. At last she had let the children come alone.

"Yes," Johnny nodded, with one hand on his new three-cornered hat. "How soon do we get there, Prince?"

The coachman turned west up Beacon Street to Beacon Hill, the highest of Boston's three hills. The street ran along a wide green field in which cows were grazing.

"That's Boston Common," Mary cried. The Common's forty acres stretched down to the banks of the Charles River.

Just then Johnny saw Uncle Tom's house. "There it is! Isn't it fine?" he said. A fence on a low stone wall ran in front of the stone mansion.

Prince stopped the carriage. Johnny jumped out and ran up the tree-bordered walk. He banged on the brass door knocker until a servant opened the wide doors. And there stood Uncle Tom and Aunt Lydia in the large central hall! The children were welcomed with a hug.

"I've stayed home from my 'counting-room' and store this morning to wait for you young ones," Uncle Tom said with a big smile.

Servants took the children's boxes up to separate guest rooms, for they were to stay two weeks in Boston.

"We've waited dinner for you," Aunt Lydia said. She led the way into the dining room. Servants seated them at a large mahogany table. There were forks for everyone, and dishes of rare china as well as the usual pewter.

Uncle Tom urged Johnny to eat more of the fresh roast meat, the chicken pies, and jellies. His face grew redder and redder as he ate his meal and drank from his silver tankard. "Eat well and you'll be strong," he declared.

When he left in his carriage he said, "Tomorrow you and Mary shall visit the zoo at the docks. There are other surprises there for good boys and girls." He winked and chuckled.

A zoo! Johnny had never seen one. "Is it like Noah's Ark in my primer?" he asked.

"Goodness, no! It's better than pictures." His aunt's eyebrows went up and her black eyes smiled at him. "Wait and see."

Johnny thought he couldn't wait, but he slept

soundly in his deep feather bed after all. Morning came before he knew it.

When he saw the waterfront the next day, Johnny thought it was wonderful. He loved the smell of the sea, of fresh and dried fish, and of tarred rope that hung over the busy seaport. The closer the carriage came to the wharfs edging the shore, the stronger the smell grew.

Mary held her nose with her small gloved fingers. "Braintree smells better," she said.

Prince pulled in the horses at the head of Long Wharf. The town's largest wharf stretched from busy King Street a half-mile out into the harbor. Warehouses, stores, and fish markets were built on one side of the wharf. The other side was free for the largest ships to tie up.

Johnny stared at strange sailors in belled blue trousers and tarred pigtails. Sea captains, clerks with ledgers, fish peddlers with tin horns or bells crowded and pushed.

"Oys! Buy any oys?" an oysterman called. He carried his wares in a sack on his back.

Hay wagons and two-wheeled carts loaded with firewood rumbled back and forth all day, Uncle Thomas said. But even above Boston's noise, Johnny could hear the cries of swooping gulls and the beat of the sea.

Uncle Thomas stopped at a wooden shed on the wharf. Inside a wooden cage in the shed sat a large white bear.

"O-o-oh!" Johnny gasped. "What kind is it? I thought bears were brown or black."

"This is a polar bear. It lives far north where there are always ice and snow. It was caught by the crew of a whaling ship, whose captain brought it here. From time to time we get animals from all over the world."

The children laughed at the tricks of a dancing dog brought from Europe. They saw bright birds and a chattering brown monkey, too. But they turned quickly away from the sight of a pirate's head pickled in a jar.

"Now it's time for the big surprise," Uncle Tom declared. He waved his gold-headed cane toward the next largest wharf two blocks away. "It's over by Clark's Wharf. We shall walk."

Johnny and Mary thought it was fun to stare into the tiny shop windows as they walked up Anne Street into Fish Street. A leather shop, a chemist's, a baker's, and a sail-maker's all slowed their steps.

"Here is the Revere silver shop," Uncle Tom said as they passed on. "I do business with silversmith Revere. Here we are!" He stopped in front of a shop. "It's Mr. Fletcher's store."

They stepped inside. It looked like other stores to Johnny. Imported cloth, candlesticks, tea, paper, and hardware were laid out on shelves. Uncle Tom led the way to a door in the back. A clerk came up to them.

49

"We wish to see the town," Uncle Tom said.

"That will be four shillings, six pence." The clerk took the coins with a smile.

Johnny and Mary looked at each other in surprise. Whatever could cost so much to see?

Spread out on a wide table was a tiny toy town. "Why, it's Boston Town!" Johnny guessed with a laugh. "See all the church steeples and the docks and ships!"

There was a whirring noise. Everything started to move. The wheels of the coaches and carts in the narrow streets began to turn. The ships sailed in and out of the harbor. A little powder mill in one corner started working.

Johnny darted from side to side of the busy town in his excitement. "How does it work?"

Mary clapped her hands daintily.

"Heh, heh! Knew you'd like it, lad. Would buy it for you, but old Fletcher won't sell. He says there are twelve hundred gears and wheels mak-

50

ing this thing run. Now I have business to attend to. We'll come back again."

"Just a little longer, please, sir?"

"Another time, another time." Before Johnny knew it, he was standing in the cold April sunshine outside the shop.

A handsome young fellow about seventeen walked up to Uncle Tom. "Your pardon, sir. May I speak to you? It's private business."

"Heh? What?" Uncle Tom looked surprised. The boy was dressed plainly and his wavy black hair was tied neatly back of his neck. He wore no hat. "What private business could you have? See my clerk." Uncle Tom started to move on.

"Wait, sir." The young fellow forced a smile. "You know Mr. Gerrish and his book shop?"

"I should. I was apprenticed to his father. I got my start by learning the book-binding business from him."

"True, sir," said the young man. "As I have

just learned it there, I would like to work for you, sir."

"Heh? Why do you not stay with Gerrish?"

"Because, sir, I heard about you often in my seven years. I was bound out to Mr. Gerrish as an apprentice, but I'm free now."

"You're an orphan? English?"

"Irish, begorra! The name's Tim O'Toole, sir. I have a fine tale for the youngsters, if you'll let them listen."

"Do listen, Uncle," Johnny begged. He liked this young man and wanted his Uncle Thomas to hire him.

Uncle Tom waved his cane at Prince, who waited near by with the carriage. "We'll sit in my carriage. You may stand beside it and tell your story, but I promise nothing."

After they had seated themselves, Tim O'Toole said, "You have heard many a sad tale, sadder, maybe, than mine, but I wish no sadder

52

tale on any soul." He gave a great sigh and rolled his dark eyes at Johnny and Mary.

They sighed in return. Their eyes didn't leave his face.

"My mother died in Ireland when I was a lad of ten. My father was a sea captain. Not knowing what to do with me, he took me to sea with him. We sailed for America. On the way over here he died suddenly. The crew buried him at sea." He took a deep breath.

"Go on, go on," ordered Uncle Tom.

"Begorra, sir, that crew—that crew did a terrible thing. The next day a shipload of orphan boys and girls hailed us. These orphans were on their way to be bound out for service in America, the captain of their ship said.

"The crew sold me to that captain of the orphan ship, sir, and he brought me to Boston Town. He bound me out to Samuel Gerrish. There I've worked these seven years."

He stopped, then rushed on. "I'm a good worker and write a fine hand. My master will have to admit that. Won't you try me, please?"

Johnny held his breath. Uncle Tom looked at him, a slight smile on his lips. Johnny said, "Say yes, please, sir."

"Call at my counting-room tomorrow, O'Toole. Ask for my chief clerk. I'll have him check on you. Maybe he can find a place for you somewhere."

"Thank you, sir." Tim bowed low. "I'll be there early. God bless you all!"

"Good luck, Tim O'Toole," Johnny called.

"A likeable lad," Uncle Tom chuckled. "He can tell a sad tale, can't he?"

"Yes, I like him," Johnny said. "Don't you, Mary? I hope I see him again the next time I come to Boston."

"Maybe that won't be very soon," Mary said with a wise look. "I've had a wonderful time,

Uncle Tom, but it's too noisy here in Boston. And smelly, too. I like to live in Braintree best, I think."

"Braintree is dull," Johnny said stoutly. "I wish we could live here. When I grow up I want to be a general or a sea captain and sail the seven seas. Then I can live in Boston when I'm not at sea or fighting a war somewhere."

A New Home

JOHNNY DIDN'T know that his wish would soon come true. A year later, in May, 1744, Father fell ill and died. He was buried in the cemetery across from the Meeting House.

Everything was mixed up for Johnny after that, until one day Mother called him to her and said sadly, "We can't live here much longer, Johnny. A new parson is coming. He will use this parsonage. I must find another place to live. Your grandfather, Bishop Hancock, says we can live with him in Lexington. But that means more mouths to feed, and he is an old man."

"What will we do then, Mother?" Seven-year-old Johnny looked up at his mother and wondered. "Where will we go?"

Mother thought a moment. "Your Grandfather, Uncle Thomas, and I have decided what is best. I hope you will think it is, too. I need Mary to help with little Ebenezer, and she doesn't care for Boston Town."

"Boston?" What had Boston to do with this? Suddenly Johnny stood quiet and waited.

"Uncle Thomas wants you to live with him. He wants to adopt you. He will send you to a grammar school and to Harvard College. I could not do that. Father wanted you to go to college, John, as he did."

Johnny nodded and swallowed a lump in his throat. "I know."

"Will you go to Uncle Tom's?"

"Yes, Mother, if I have to. I would like to live with him." He didn't look at her.

Mother gave him a hug. "We will miss you,

son, but will try to see you often. You will have a fine future with Uncle Tom."

Johnny buried his head on Mother's shoulder so she wouldn't see his tears.

The next morning Uncle Thomas arrived. He brought a box of fine clothes for Johnny. There were new black slippers with silver buckles, a ruffled shirt, a blue silk coat and a white waistcoat—and a small wig!

Johnny threw the white wig in a corner. "I won't wear it," he said with spirit. How the boys in Braintree would laugh!

Mother and Uncle Tom smiled. "That was your aunt's idea," Uncle said, "just to try it out. You'd have to have your head shaved first, you know, Johnny."

"No, sir!" Johnny clutched his brown hair tied neatly behind his neck. "I'll keep my own, thank you."

A short time later Johnny was sitting stiffly

in his new clothes in Uncle Tom's carriage, ready to go to Boston.

"Good-by, good-by, and God bless you," Mother and Mary said to him. Little Ebenezer laughed and said, "By-by."

Jay Adams stood waving at the gate, too. He had come over from the Latin School near the Meeting House to see Johnny off.

As Prince drove away, an old black pig ran squealing from in front of the horses' hoofs. Two white piglets followed her.

"It's Daisy!" Johnny said, and even felt sorry to leave her.

A curve in the highway hid the parsonage. Near Black Creek rail fences marked off stony pastures and fields of grain. No longer could Johnny climb the highest hill of firs and watch the sails in Boston Harbor. Perhaps never again would he fish with Little Turtle.

Uncle Tom looked down at Johnny. "Boston

is not far away," he said. "Your mother and Mary and Ebenezer will come to visit us."

Johnny nodded. "May Jay Adams visit me?"

"Of course, my boy."

Johnny began to feel better and enjoy the ride to Boston.

"Here we are!" Uncle Tom said when they drew up before his fine mansion. He and Johnny got out and Prince drove the carriage into the coach house on the left side of the house.

Aunt Lydia met Johnny in the wide hall with its curving staircase. "Welcome to your new home, dear Johnny," she said.

"Thank you, Aunt Lydia." Johnny swept off his three-cornered hat and made a bow as Mother had taught him. Then he was caught up in Aunt Lydia's arms. Her fat cheeks shook. The mole on her right eyebrow went up and down.

"Here, here" and "Heh, heh," said Uncle Tom. He patted them both on the back.

Aunt Lydia let Johnny go, to his relief. She stood back to see his new clothes. "Now you are dressed as the son of a Boston merchant should be dressed," she said with a nod. "I see you didn't wear the wig I sent along."

Johnny turned pink. "I like the clothes, and I thank you for them," he said politely. "But the wig—it scratched and was too hot."

His aunt didn't smile. "Well, you shall get used to it someday. Right now you need not wear it. Tomorrow we'll go shopping for more clothes. Then we shall see about Latin School."

School had to wait, however. Johnny fell ill and was unable to go. When his fever left him and he was better, a private teacher came to the house. His tutor helped Johnny to learn Latin.

He needed to know Latin because the grammar schools of those days, which were called Latin Schools, spent most of their time on the study of Latin and Greek.

Behind Uncle Tom's house a large garden swept up Beacon Hill. Johnny liked to sit and study there in the summer house.

When he tired of studying, he would drop *Cheever's Latin Grammar* in his lap and stare at the tar-barrel beacon at the top of the hill. It was fastened to a tall mast.

He could imagine that he was the person chosen to climb the mast and set the beacon afire. Its soaring flames would warn all the countryside around of enemy attack.

Or he could watch the white wings of ships skim across wide, blue Boston Bay. To the north he could look across the Charles River to Cambridge and Harvard College. To the south he could see the rugged blue hills of Dorchester and Braintree.

One afternoon Aunt Lydia swept out to the summer house. She wore a high bonnet and a shawl, although it was a warm July day. "Come

Johnny. We're going to call on the Quincys this afternoon," she said.

"In Braintree, ma'am?" Johnny's heart beat faster. He jumped to his feet.

His aunt smiled. "No, these Quincys live here in Boston, although they used to live in Braintree. The family is so large it is no wonder you mix them up. We are going to the Edmund Quincys. They have so many children I've lost count of them. Colonel Josiah Quincy's family will be there, too."

Children romped all over the Quincys' big house on Star Lane, Johnny found out. There were Ned, Sam, Hannah, Jacob, Esther, and more. He gave up trying to sort them out.

The boys played "Scotch-hoppers" and "bat-and-ball" in the cobbled stableyard beside the house. They played Indian with bows and arrows. They chased the girls around the mulberry tree in the garden.

64

For this they were roundly scolded. The girls in their long, heavy skirts and cloth shoes could hardly run.

"We'll come over to your house during August vacation," Sam Quincy told Johnny. He was seven years old, too. "We can fly our kites on Boston Common."

And so they did. Johnny was happy to find new friends. "What fun to belong to a large family!" he said.

Uncle Tom took pains to be kind to him.

One noon at dinner he said, "Johnny, I'm not going back to my counting-room this afternoon. I'm taking you down to watch a ship unload. I own part of the goods it brought. I'm lucky it came through safely."

He looked at his wife. "This new war with France and Spain brings us war orders from England. That means we're paid in silver and gold. You know how scarce *they* are!"

Uncle Tom shook his head with its large white wig. "These sea captains and their sailors have their silver coins melted down and made into bowls and tankards. That makes silver money scarce again! Revere, the silversmith, tells me he keeps very busy."

"Oh, that reminds me," said Aunt Lydia. "Will you stop by Revere's shop and order me a new copper kettle?"

"Yes, my dear." After the prayer, Uncle Tom rose from the table. "Come along, Johnny, my boy. Let us be going."

"Right away, sir. Good-by, Aunt Lydia." Johnny made a bow.

He and Uncle Tom drove down Beacon Hill and soon turned into wide King Street. At the head of Long Wharf, they turned north along the waterfront. They passed Uncle Tom's shop, "The Bible and Three Crowns."

This had been the first of the four shops that

Uncle Tom now owned. He had started here as a bookseller. Then he had gone into the trading business. Now he was the richest man in the Massachusetts Colony.

"How is Tim O'Toole doing, sir?" Johnny asked. "I would like to see him."

"We'll stop on our way back," Uncle Tom promised. "He's doing very well, very well as a clerk. Writes a fine hand. Even has been made a sergeant in the militia. Started as a drummer boy, you know."

Johnny didn't know. But Tim had made him laugh when they met a few months ago.

The carriage stopped at the head of Clark's Wharf in Fish Street. Uncle Tom sent Prince off with it to a near-by stable.

Uncle Tom had a warehouse that was built right on the wharf. Here he stored the whale oil and ships' masts that he sent to England. Here, too, he stored the goods that he brought in from the West Indies, England, and Holland—rolls of cloth, nails, hinges, bolts, tools, and tea.

Johnny stood in front of a shop window that faced the busy wharf. A signboard swung over the shop door. On it were painted the words, "Revere, Silversmith."

"Here's where you are to order the teapot, Uncle." Johnny smiled, pleased to have remembered about the teapot.

Just then a husky boy dashed out the door. He carried a basket over his arm. He wore the full leather breeches of Boston apprentice boys and a leather apron.

He bumped square into Johnny and almost knocked him off his feet. "Hey, take care!" Johnny cried angrily.

The brown-haired boy stopped. He nodded quickly to Uncle Tom. "A good morrow to you, Mr. Hancock. I'm Paul, the oldest Revere boy." His brown eyes flickered over at Johnny. "My pardon," he added smiling, "but little fellows should look sharp."

Then with a hearty laugh he ran on.

"I'll trip him the next time I see him," Johnny grumbled. "He's not so much bigger."

"Heh, heh. Don't fret about him. Come along now and watch this brig unload."

The high ship pressed close against the wharf. Cranes creaked as they swung boxes and barrels onto the broad wharf. The captain stood on deck and shouted orders to the dock workers.

Johnny watched, his eyes shining with excitement. He saw dozens of fishing boats and bigger ships tied to the wharfs. He looked up at the forest of wooden roofs and church steeples rising from the shore. And all the while the exciting, shrill, loud noises of the waterfront were in his ears.

He pulled at his uncle's silk coat. "I like all this, Uncle," he said. "I wish to be a merchant when I'm a man. I would like to work with you if I may."

Uncle Tom beamed. "Just what I hoped you would say, my lad."

Johnny went on, almost to himself. "Maybe I can be a sailor-general or a pirate."

"Ho! Ho!" Uncle Tom's double chins shook. "You'll find pirates enough among our Boston merchants, Johnny!" he said. "Come, let's order the teapot now. Then we can walk back to the 'Bible and Three Crowns.' "

Almost everything was on sale at Uncle Tom's shop, from things for the home to ships' supplies. The smell of spices, tobacco, and coal dust tickled Johnny's nose when he pushed open the door and went inside.

Uncle Tom's "counting-room" was in the room next to the shop. There the letter-writing of the vast trading business was carried on. Several clerks sat at high desks, pushing goose quill pens across miles of foolscap paper.

"Come, we'll call out young O'Toole," Uncle Tom said.

Johnny followed him happily through the shop and into the counting-room. He was enjoying every moment of this day.

71

The Militia Sails

THE BEAT of drums and the squeal of fifes awoke Johnny early one morning. He jumped from his high feather bed and rushed to the little balcony over the front door.

Three thousand militiamen were camped on Boston Common. The Royal Governor of Massachusetts had called them up this March of 1745. He planned to attack a French fort in Canada.

"Today's the day!" John, who was now eight, thought excitedly. "The soldiers are going to sail to Nova Scotia and——"

"Johnny!" Aunt Lydia stood behind him. She

wore a dressing gown. "Don't stand out here in this damp! You'll catch your death of cold."

Johnny turned to her, almost dancing in his eagerness. "Oh, Aunt! The militiamen are starting. Hear the drums! Can't we go now?"

"Mercy, it's much too early." Aunt Lydia closed the balcony door and pushed him into his room. "They're not going yet."

Later, Cato, a young Negro, came in with a pan of hot coals. "Mornin', Mister Johnny."

He started a fire to take the dampness out of the room. Johnny still marveled at burning coal in his fireplace. Only the rich could afford to burn coal instead of firewood, for it came from Newcastle, England.

Johnny put on warm red wool stockings and a wool broadcloth suit. At breakfast he was silent, but he kept his eyes on Uncle Tom.

At last his uncle rose from the table and rubbed his long nose. "Is there a lad here who wants to watch the militia board ship this morning?" he asked.

"Yes, sir, I do!" Johnny grinned happily.

Down at Boston harbor an air of excitement hung over the docks. Sixty ships waited there to take on men and supplies.

A crowd was gathered at Clark's Wharf. Wearing wool cloaks to protect themselves against the sharp ocean wind, Johnny and Uncle Tom mingled with the crowd.

Two merchant friends joined Uncle Tom. They talked about the French fort called Louisburg on Cape Breton Island in Canada. "It is a threat to us and our fishing boats. It will be a threat as long as England is at war with France," one merchant said.

The other merchant looked cross. "How can our militiamen fight real French soldiers? We need men who know how to use big cannon—and how many big cannon do we have?"

74

"We've taken the cannon from the town's South Battery and from Castle Island Fort in the harbor," Uncle Tom told him. "We've borrowed others from neighboring colonies. I helped find supplies for this adventure. However, we need big guns to storm Fort Louisburg."

"It'll be a miracle if our men capture it," said the merchant. "They will fail."

"Some of the officers know a little gunnery. I have faith in our New England men," Uncle Tom said stoutly.

Johnny nodded proudly. "Even more so," he thought, "since Sergeant Tim O'Toole is going to fight." Where was Tim? Johnny couldn't see him among the line of blue-coated men who were marching aboard the ships at Clark's wharf. Maybe he was at another wharf.

Johnny slipped away through the crowd. He ran along the waterfront, hoping to see Tom. At Long Wharf he saw the "Massachusetts Frigate,"

Boston's own warship, tied up alongside the wharf. Militiamen were boarding it, too.

Guns poked their noses out of portholes along its sides. An arm waved from one of the double rows of windows across the ship's stern.

Was someone calling? "Johnny Hancock! Oh, Johnny Hancock! Halloo-o-o!"

And there was the black head of Tim O'Toole. Tim grinned and waved his sergeant's cap.

"Good-by, Tim O'Toole," Johnny yelled. He waved as hard as he could. "Good luck! Fight for New England!"

With a last wave, he ran back to seek his uncle. He felt happy to have said good-by to a soldier who was his friend.

Weeks passed by, and all Boston waited for word from Canada. In May a fishing boat brought word that the ships were waiting near Cape Breton Island for the ice to break up in the harbor at Louisburg.

The Hancocks were getting ready to take one of their Saturday drives into the country.

First they would stop to see Johnny's cousins, Lucy and Will Bowes. The Boweses lived in a big white parsonage in Bedford. Later Uncle Tom might drive on the few miles to Lexington.

Johnny hoped so. He wanted to see his mother, his sister Mary, and his Grandfather and Grandmother Hancock.

Lucy Bowes could write a very neat hand for a girl. She showed Johnny the silver inkstand dish that belonged to her father, Parson Bowes. It was a box that held quills and a square inkpot.

"Show me how you write now," Lucy said with a smile. She gave Johnny a scrap of paper.

Johnny bit his lips. He scratched out his words in a crooked, scraggly line.

Lucy cocked her head to one side. "It's a little better, Johnny. Your letters aren't so huge as before."

Johnny threw down the quill pen. "Oh, I don't care. I just am not a good writer. Come, let's see if we all drive over to Lexington."

They soon were on their way. At Lexington the Meeting House stood at one end of the Green, or Common. Next to it was the village tavern. The parsonage stood a few hundred yards up the turnpike, facing the Meeting House.

When the visitors reached the parsonage, they were greeted happily. "Johnny looks much better," Mother said, pleased.

"He will soon be strong enough to go to Latin School every day," Aunt Lydia told her.

Johnny, Mary, Lucy, and Will played "seek-out" until almost dark. Hand in hand, they raced over the Lexington hills. They hid behind stone walls and hedges along the turnpike.

The Hancocks stayed the night. The next day they heard Grandfather Hancock preach in the morning and the afternoon. Both times he thundered for two hours at the country farmers who came to church.

The children crowded into the balcony of the bare church. They pushed, pinched, and giggled, but they were careful that the "tithing man" was not watching. If he saw them he would rap them with the long stick he carried.

Johnny, Uncle Tom, and Aunt Lydia drove back to Boston on Monday, because no one was supposed to travel on the holy Sabbath. On the way Johnny decided he was going to show Lucy Bowes! "I'll write a neat hand if I do nothing else!" he vowed.

Then he heard Uncle Tom remark to his aunt, "We ought to hear more news from Canada soon."

"I wonder what's happened to Tim O'Toole?" Johnny said. "When will he come back?"

Tim O'Toole and Fort Louisburg

ONE JULY night that same year Johnny was deep in dreams. Suddenly the boom of a cannon awoke him. He sat up, his heart thumping. It was almost dawn.

He heard someone gallop up Beacon Hill, shouting, "Fort Louisburg has fallen!" Then church bells began to ring and muskets to fire.

Molly, the Irish maid, came in with a basin of hot water for Johny to wash in. "Our brave militia have beat the French soldiers," she said excitedly.

"Huzza for them!" Johnny shouted. He pranced barefooted about his room.

"It's a great victory for Massachusetts Colony," Uncle Tom declared at breakfast. He helped himself from a silver bowl of hasty pudding that Molly held. "Everyone knows we gave most of the men and ships. And it was the Governor's idea to capture Louisburg."

"To think that Tim O'Toole saw it all!" Johnny burst out. "How soon will he be back?"

"That's hard to say, Johnny. Months, perhaps. Ah, no one will work this happy day!"

Months later, on a cold November day, the first ships came back from Canada. Among them was the "Massachusetts Frigate."

To Johnny's delight, Jay Adams came to town with his father, Deacon Adams. They went with Johnny and Uncle Tom to see the militia come off the ship.

The tired men marched from Long Wharf up short King Street. They stepped between rows of British soldiers and cadets.

"Huzza!" Johnny and Jay shouted a welcome along with everyone else.

"Look!" whispered Johnny. "Their red and blue uniforms are all rags."

"Yes, but how proud they look! They know they did a great thing."

"Where's Tim O'Toole?" Johnny hopped from one foot to the other trying to see.

That night every window in the big Hancock house was lighted. Friends had been coming and going all day.

A huge bonfire blazed on the Common across the street. Fireworks banged and rockets glittered overhead. Johnny, Jay, Sam Quincy, and a group of boys sat near the fire, watching. So Johnny was able to see Tim O'Toole clearly when he walked past with a group of soldiers.

"Tim! Sergeant Tim!" Johnny ran and stood in front of the young man.

"Sure, and it's the master's fine boy!" Tim

cried. His white teeth flashed and he clapped Johnny on the shoulder.

"How are you? Oh, I'm glad you came by! Please sit here with us and watch the fireworks," Johnny said eagerly. "Then you can tell us all about your taking Fort Louisburg."

"Oh? And is that all you want of me?" Tim asked. But he was kind enough to sit with the boys. He had been sent home early, he said, because he had been ill with camp fever. "Now, then, what do you want to hear first?"

"All of it," Johnny said. "How our militia shot down the high walls of the fort overnight and how——"

" 'Twas not that easy, Johnny. First of all, our ships had to meet in Canso Bay. That's five hundred miles north of here. The British finally decided to help and Admiral Warren met us with five warships.

"We had word that the harbor of Louisburg

84

was solid ice. No ships could go in or out, so the French couldn't know we were near."

"How near were you?" Johnny put in.

"Only fifty miles away. We waited three weeks. Then, on April 30, we landed half our men in a bay below Fort Louisburg and the other half the next day. The surf was high and the shore rocky, but all our boats landed safely.

"The French fired a signal cannon when they saw our sails. All the people working outside the town rushed inside the walls. A party of French soldiers came out to meet us, but we drove them away.

"We marched over rocks, hills, and through swamps. We made camp two miles from the fort. A big swamp lay between us and the French."

"What did you do then?" Johnny asked.

"We looked up at those thirty-foot-high walls of the fort and, begorra, we wondered how we would ever get in!

"You see, Fort Louisburg sat on the south point of the bay. There was a group of cannon, known as the Grand Battery, in the hills behind the bay. There was also a strong fort on an island in the harbor. We had to take the battery and the island fort as well as the town."

"How did you do it?" Jay Adams asked.

Tom laughed. "Well, my captain, Captain Vaughn, found some naval storehouses in the hills behind the Grand Battery. They held pitch, tar, oil, and gunpowder. We set fire to them. There was a terrible flash when the gunpowder blew up, and clouds of smoke filled the sky."

At that moment high flames shot up from the big bonfire on the Common. A sky rocket burst like diamonds over the boys' heads.

"O-o-oh!" everyone cried. The boys watched in silence for a moment. Johnny felt that he could almost see the storehouses burn.

"The black smoke covered the Grand Battery,"

Tim went on. "It scared the French soldiers and they ran away. Later, Captain Vaughn sent in an Indian scout to see if all was clear. It was. One of my men (there were thirteen of us) climbed the flagpole and nailed his red coat to it for a flag."

The boys laughed loudly.

"The hardest part was yet to come," Tim told them. "We needed bigger guns to reach the main part of the fort and the island battery. The only heavy guns we had were the ships' guns. We brought them ashore on flatboats. Some were smashed on the rocks by the surf, but we got most of them ashore. Some of us waded in through the icy water carrying powder casks high over our heads.

"Then we pulled the heavy guns through the swamp with ropes. There were three hundred of us tied to one gun! The guns sank in the mud. All the time we were under fire from the fort. So we made wooden sleds and dragged the guns through the swamp and over the hills at night.

"One by one, we placed the big guns in the hills overlooking Louisburg. Then, when the guns were ready, we poured cannon fire into the town. But even that wasn't enough."

Tim stopped and coughed.

"What happened next?" Johnny asked.

"For a month we kept firing into the town," Tim went on. "The French fired back at us. At last many of our men were barefoot and in rags. Our colonel ordered us to carry some of the cannon to Lighthouse Point. That was a high cliff on the north point of the bay. Again we dragged the cannon with ropes—a mile and a half up that cliff. Then we could fire down into the island's fort. The French ran into the sea."

"Huzza!" the boys said softly.

"Now our cannon fire never stopped. From every side we poured nine thousand cannon balls and six hundred bombs into Fort Louisburg. For green men who didn't know much about big guns, we learned fast.

"I fell sick the day the French surrendered. The next day our men marched into the town and the French marched out to sail for France. The day after that it began to rain. It rained for ten days. If the rains had come sooner, we could not have captured Louisburg, begorra! Thank the Lord!"

"Nobody can beat our New England men," Johnny said with pride.

Tim laughed, then coughed. "At least, we know we can lick the Frenchies. It's lucky I am I'm here, what with the fever and all. But I'm on the mend, lads. I must go along now."

The boys thanked him for his thrilling story. Now a bright sky rocket streaked like a golden arrow through the blackness overhead.

"We are like an arrow," Johnny thought. "We can protect our country ourselves."

And by his "country" he meant the colony of Massachusetts, not England.

Boston Is Saved

JOHNNY CAREFULLY wiped his quill pen with a bit of cloth. He dipped the point into his ink-horn. Once again he began to copy from his Dillworth speller.

"Master Hancock!" Johnny felt a sharp rap on his hand. "You little wretch!"

He looked up while he rubbed his stinging fingers. Schoolmaster John Lovell stood over him. He held a ruler in his hand and scowled.

"You've spoiled your paper again," Mr. Lovell scolded. "Hold your pen right, and you won't splash ink on your work. And never use a pen-wiper on a pen!"

Johnny gulped. "But, sir, how do I——"

"See here." The schoolmaster grabbed the pen. He wiped off the pen point with his little finger. Then he pushed back the old powdered wig he wore. He wiped off his finger on the thin strands of gray hair under his wig!

Johnny stared. He tried not to smile, but his teacher's head was dotted with black ink!

"My aunt——" he began to say, then thought better of it. "I'll do better, sir," he promised. He took a fine linen handkerchief from his coat pocket. He wiped his wet hands and then started to work again.

He had gone to South Latin School since he was eight, over a year now. It was on School Street next to King's Chapel and only two blocks from home.

The last hour of school, from three to four o'clock, was given over to writing lessons and to the mending of quill pens. Only the older boys were allowed to mend and cut new points on their quill pens.

"Will this day never end?" Johnny groaned. How could he think about his bad writing when the French fleet might attack Boston port soon?

Only fifteen months before, the great fort of Louisburg had fallen to the New Englanders. Because of that, the French King was now sending forty warships and a hundred other ships to capture Boston.

A whaling ship and several fishing boats had raced down from the North Atlantic with the news of the mighty French fleet's approach. "They're strung out for miles," the sailors from the boats said. "And they're filled to the masts with French soldiers."

Johnny wondered whether more New England militia had arrived today to camp on the Common's wide green acres. "What a grand sight their tents make!" he thought. "Six thousand men are camped there, ready to fight for Boston and America if need be."

The soldiers' campfires, the ruffle of drums and fifes, the shouts and orders all added to the excitement of these October days.

Johnny frowned and bit the end of his quill pen. "I wish Aunt Lydia would let me visit the men in camp," he thought. "But she says they're not Boston men and I shouldn't bother them."

Just this morning she had said, "Thank Heaven, we're safe as long as this south wind keeps blowing." For ten days the wind had come from the south. "The French will have trouble sailing south to Boston against it."

Suddenly the school bell broke into his thoughts. A general prayer was said, then the boys rushed pell-mell outside.

At once Johnny noticed that the wind had changed. A gusty wind was now coming from the north. It tore showers of October leaves from

94

the trees. And it would speed the French ships toward Boston!

He gazed up at the tar-barrel beacon atop Beacon Hill. "How soon," he wondered, "might it flash the alarm?"

He walked slowly up Beacon Street along one side of the Common. He looked longingly at the bustling camp. Some of his schoolmates were shouting and running toward it.

"If I can't visit the camp, perhaps I can ride over to Sam Quincy's after tea. We can talk about it all. Prince will help me saddle Imp." Johnny loved Imp, his new red-brown pony.

"Some day I'm going to jump Imp over the stone wall back of the pasture," Johnny promised himself. "When Aunt Lydia is out for afternoon tea would be the best time, I think."

With a last look at the camp, he went up the stone steps of the mansion. Inside, Molly brought Indian pudding and gingerbread on a silver tea tray, while Johnny gave Aunt Lydia a peck on her round cheek.

Uncle Tom came in from his library. There was a worried look on his pleasant face. He wore a red velvet cap on his shaved head in place of his large powdered wig.

"Remember, the Governor has set aside tomorrow as a Fast Day," Aunt Lydia told them both. "We'll go to Old South Church in the morning. Pastor Prince will pray for us to be saved from the French fleet."

The next day hundreds of people prayed at Old South. Johnny listened hard as the pastor said, "Send Thy tempest, Lord. Sink their proud ships with the power of Thy winds."

At that very moment the day darkened. Johnny could hardly see his aunt and uncle. High winds tore at the doors and windows of the church and shook the very building itself. The great church bell struck wildly once, twice. No

one was in the steeple, and no one pulled the bell! Everyone looked upward with astonishment and alarm.

"We hear Thy voice, O Lord!" the parson cried out. It was an answer to their prayer, Johnny felt sure.

A week later several ships brought news that a terrible storm had sunk part of the French fleet. A fever had made ill or killed hundreds of French soldiers. Their admiral was dead. The fleet could no longer destroy the colonies.

All New England gave joyful thanks. "If God be for us, who can be against us?" everyone said.

Johnny was more sure than ever that New England was a match for anyone.

Johnny Saves a Sailor

TEN-YEAR-OLD Johnny stretched his feet out toward the hot fire in Uncle Tom's library. He dropped his Greek textbook to the floor. Then he opened the new book, called "Robinson Crusoe," that Uncle Tom had given him just the night before.

"I must put my name in this," he said aloud. He found a quill pen in his uncle's desk.

He scratched out on the first page:

John Hancock his book, November, 1747.
If this book I do lend and you do borrow,
Pray read it through today,
And send it home tomorrow.

He smiled proudly as he looked at his writing. At last he could write a neat line, even though he felt he never could make small letters.

Today was a school holiday. He was waiting for Aunt Lydia's callers to leave. Then he and Aunt Lydia would drive to a shoemaker's shop on King Street. Johnny was growing so fast that he needed a new pair of shoes.

Mrs. Edmund Quincy, who was Sam's aunt, had brought her newest baby to be admired. Six-month-old Dorothy Quincy was called "Dolly." Johnny could hear the ladies in the parlor.

"Huh! The way they're ooh-ing and aah-ing over Dolly!" he snorted.

"Mistress is ready," young Cato came to tell him at last.

Aunt Lydia, in her large bonnet and warm red cloak, waited in the open carriage. Uncle Tom had ordered a fine yellow coach from England, but it had not come yet. Today Uncle Tom had used his two-wheeled chaise to drive downhill to his store.

First, Aunt Lydia stopped at a dressmaker's shop. There the dressmaker showed her a new puppet, called a "fashion doll." It had just come from London and was dressed in the latest style in clothes.

The doll so pleased Aunt Lydia that dusk was coming by the time she reached the cobbler's shop. The shop faced Long Wharf.

Johnny's feet were measured for a pair of shoes with silver buckles and also for a pair of boots. While Aunt Lydia ordered her new shoes, Johnny peered out the shop window. He could see the lights of the British warships that were anchored out in the harbor.

Suddenly he saw eight or ten British sailors running up from Long Wharf. They all carried clubs. They caught three men walking along the waterfront.

Two of the men were dragged back toward the wharf and a waiting longboat. The third man fought his way clear. He ran as fast as he could through the dusk. When he reached the cobbler's shop, he suddenly turned and darted in through the door. The little bell above the door jangled fiercely, "Ding-a-ling, ding!"

The shoemaker, Johnny, and Aunt Lydia all stared at the panting young man in seaman's clothes. A black eye and a bloody nose gave him a wild look. He had lost his knitted cap.

"Mercy!" exclaimed Aunt Lydia.

"Hide me!" cried the young man. "The King's sailors are sweeping the waterfront. They aim to fill their ships' crews. They'll be here looking for me in a moment!"

The cobbler found his tongue. "In here." He opened a door at the back of the shop. "Stay in this back room for a while and hide."

The young sailor croaked, "My thanks to ye,

mate. Send warning. The British are taking landsmen as well as seamen."

With a quick nod to them all, he slipped through the back door. Everything had happened so fast that Aunt Lydia hadn't found words. The cobbler gave her a worried look.

"I hope you are not angry with me, Madame Hancock," he said. "I couldn't let him be caught. He's an American seaman in our Boston fishing fleet. The British warships often try to kidnap our sailors. Life on those frigates is so bad the crews run off any chance they get. This is the start of a 'hot press,' I vow!"

Aunt Lydia's eyes shot sparks. "You did right. The idea! How wicked to beat men and take them aboard ships against their will! We must stop this business."

Johnny had heard talk of the impressment of American seamen before. This was the first time he had seen it happen. His face flushed with

anger. He wished he were a grown man. He would go out and stop this business!

"Come, Johnny. We must go home." Aunt Lydia moved toward the shop door.

"Wait, please, Auntie." Johnny caught her arm. An idea was growing in his mind. "Why can't we take that sailor with us in the carriage?"

"I don't know." Aunt Lydia frowned and thought a moment. Then to Johnny's relief she smiled and snapped, "We'll do it. A fine idea!"

Johnny ran outside to tell Prince, the coachman. How quickly the waterfront had cleared! Somewhere out in the dimness covering the docks, he heard men's shouts and running feet.

Soon tall, stout Aunt Lydia hurried out to her carriage. Johnny walked on one side of her and Prince on the other. Close behind them crept the young Boston sailor. He slipped up on the driver's seat next to Prince.

In a minute they were off at a fast trot through

the empty streets. The soft glimmer of a house light here and there helped to show them the way home.

Back home, the sailor was hidden in the coach house until morning. Uncle Tom in his red velvet cap and blue dressing gown paced his study. He shook his head as Johnny and his aunt told about their adventure.

"It's that Captain Knowles! He's a hard man. He cares for nothing but the King's navy. He'll seize any man he finds, whether a seaman or a shipbuilder's apprentice."

Aunt Lydia sat up straight in her brocaded chair. "We must not allow it. Do something!"

Uncle Tom slapped his hand on his desk. "I will, Madame. In the morning I shall call on the Governor. I'll insist that he must ask Captain Knowles to return the Americans he's taken aboard his warships. We have our rights!"

"Good for you, Uncle!" Johnny cried. He was

proud of his Uncle Tom. "I wish I could hear you tell the Governor."

But Uncle Tom did not get to see the Governor. At midday, when Johnny came home from school for the dinner recess, his aunt told him Uncle Tom had sent her word.

"An angry crowd of dock workers, sailors, and the like gathered near the docks early this morning," she said. "They are armed with sticks, mops, and rusty swords. They've seized some British naval officers and threatened the Governor. The town's in an uproar. You must stay home from school this afternoon, Johnny."

Late that night Uncle Tom came back. "The members of the Governor's Council met in the Town House tonight," he said. "Several thousand people howled outside."

Johnny knew the Town House. It was the large government building at the head of King Street. Every year each town and village elected a man to sit in the General Assembly. These men met in the Town House.

"The Governor tried to calm the mob," Uncle Tom went on. "He hopes to get the kidnapped men back." He looked troubled. "We can't have mob rule. Yet we are free Englishmen. We won't be treated as slaves."

The next day at school the boys talked excitedly about British Captain Knowles's threat to bombard the town if his officers were not freed. Several days later a town meeting of all the people was called.

The people of Boston agreed to return the navy officers to their ships. Captain Knowles took the kidnapped Boston men from the holds of his ships. He sent them ashore. Then he set sail. Boston was happy to see him go.

The Thanksgiving holidays came soon after this trouble. The Hancocks would spend the day with Johnny's grandparents in Lexington. Then

Johnny would go to Braintree to visit Jay Adams for several days.

Johnny was happy about that. What fun he and Jay would have skating, sleighing, and roasting apples and chestnuts in the fire!

"Just wait until Jay hears how we saved a sailor from the British 'press,'" he said to Aunt Lydia. "He won't believe it."

Jay did believe it, though. He listened closely to Johnny's stories of the Boston riot, when Johnny went to Braintree.

"Won't King George be angry about the riot?" Jay asked thoughtfully.

"No," Johnny said, surprised. "It's not his fault. It's the Navy's."

The two boys climbed the hills of the North Common one day. Only a light powder of snow lay on the ground. They saw some men working.

The men were breaking up some of the huge granite boulders that lay scattered over the hills.

109

A team of eight oxen and a long wagon stood waiting near by.

"The boulders are going to be broken up and used for building stones," Jay explained. "The village gave the men permission to take them."

"Uncle Thomas has Braintree granite in our house," Johnny said.

The workmen lighted large bonfires around a boulder. As the fire grew hotter, the stone snapped with a noise like a pistol shot. When a crack showed in it, the men broke the stone apart with hammers and a crowbar.

One man dropped an iron ball on another heated stone.

"That way of breaking rocks is not so good," Jay said. "A man can't tell just how the rock will split. Hammers and a crowbar are best."

The boys watched the men heave and struggle to get the stone onto the wagon. Then they shouldered their ice skates and went down to the

110

Adams farm. It was time to help with the evening chores.

On the way they talked about fishing through the ice. "How is Little Turtle?" Johnny asked suddenly. "Did you see him last summer? Do you still fish together?"

Jay grinned. "Aye, and he's not little. He's taller than you. He says he wants to be an army scout on our border. His uncle was a scout at the attack on Fort Louisburg."

Johnny gasped. "There was an Indian there with Sergeant Tim. He climbed into the Grand Battery and opened the gate. What if he were the same Indian? Wouldn't that be exciting?"

Jay shrugged and laughed. "Who knows? Maybe yes, maybe no. Race you to our gate!"

When Johnny left the next day, Jay promised to visit him during school holidays in August.

Johnny Meets Sam Adams

CLARK's WHARF buzzed with action one August afternoon in 1748. Dock workers loaded army supplies on a Hancock ship.

"Phew!" Jay Adams, twelve, wrinkled his nose at the strong smell of tar and salt fish. This was the first day of his long-looked-for visit with Johnny in Boston.

Johnny just leaned against a molasses barrel and laughed.

"So your uncle sends supplies to our men still holding Fort Louisburg," Jay asked.

"Yes," replied Johnny. "The army orders are helping him to buy Clark's Wharf. What shall we do now? We've seen the sail loft and the ten shops here on the wharf. We've seen the kings and queens done in wax at the waxworks. We've still some time before we meet Uncle Tom for supper at the Royal Tavern."

They dodged a carter pushing an empty cart.

"Go swimming?" Jay had his eyes on several boys. They had climbed the rigging of a near-by fishing boat and dived into the cool bay.

Johnny shook his head. "Aunt Lydia doesn't want me in the water, because I get sore throats and fever sometimes. It's silly, but she worries about me."

"Don't you want to go swimming?" Jay said in a surprised voice.

"Of course, but if you know Aunt Lydia, you do what she asks. I *would* like to," Johnny said a little sadly.

"Never mind," Jay told him cheerfully. "You will get to, someday. Let's walk over to the

113

market hall in Dock Square. Fanueil Hall, you call it? That is, if we don't get run over by horses or knocked down by a carter."

He stopped as they reached the head of the wharf. "Wait. Where's Cato?"

Uncle Tom had told Cato to keep an eye on the boys while he was at work.

Johnny chuckled and winked. "Cato often slips away when nobody's looking. I don't mind."

They turned into a narrow crooked street known as Queen Street. A man coming from a shop was reading a small newspaper.

Jay looked at the paper and yelped. "Johnny! he's reading cousin Sam Adams' paper!"

"Your cousin's? How do you know?"

"I saw the words 'Independent Advertiser,' and there's a picture of a lady and a bird at the top of the page. I wonder——" Jay read the shop sign, " 'Rogers and Fowles, printers.' Maybe they would know about it. Let's go in."

114

"Why?" Johnny suddenly felt shy.

"Oh, come along." Jay stepped inside.

The empty room smelled musty. A counter and desk held some newspapers and books. The clumping noise of a printing press came through an open doorway from an inner room.

Johnny peeked through the doorway. He saw two men working at a wooden hand press. One turned the screw while the other pulled out each printed sheet as it was stamped. Light streamed from an open skylight above.

One of the men looked up. He came towards the boys, wiping his inky fingers on his leather apron. "What can I do for you pretty boys?"

This made the boys laugh. "I'm looking for Sam Adams, a cousin of my father's," Jay told him. "I'm from Braintree. I hear that——"

The man turned. "Oh, Adams," he called.

For the first time, Johnny noticed a young man sitting at a table near the window. His quill

115

pen raced over a long strip of foolscap. After a moment he laid down his pen and looked up from the page.

"What is it, Rogers?" he asked mildly.

Jay stepped around the press and bowed slightly to the young man. Sam Adams must be over twenty, Johnny decided. He wore no wig, just his plain brown hair. His clothes were not neat, or even clean.

Sam Adams seemed really pleased to meet the boys. "Father's read your paper," Jay said eagerly. "That's how I knew it when I met that man outside. Father says you're the secret editor and that——"

Sam Adams waved his hand and smiled. "One can hear anything in Boston," he said. "I write a little for the paper, shall we say. Does he like the 'Advertiser?' "

"We-e-ll——" Jay hesitated.

Sam shrugged. "I see. He thinks I'm too much

116

in favor of the liberty of the colonies? Is that it, my boy?"

Jay looked puzzled. "I don't know about that, sir. He—he thinks you're against British rule and the King."

"Ah-h-h!" Sam pulled at his lower lip. "Not if King George gives us the rights of Englishmen. Do you know what liberty is, boys?"

"It's being free——" Johnny started to say.

"It's being free to help rule ourselves. Free to

write and speak what we ourselves believe to be right. It's a gift from God. No one should force people against their wills. We are not England's slaves, whatever she thinks."

Johnny began to understand. "Aye! Like the British sailors kidnapping our Boston men. Our men didn't want to go aboard their ships. Neither the King nor our Governor said the sailors could take our men. So it was wrong for the Navy to kidnap them."

Sam Adams smiled pleasantly. "You learn fast. Do you plan to go to Cambridge to study at Harvard College?"

"Yes, sir, in two more years. I'll be thirteen then," Johnny said.

"And you, cousin John?" Adams turned to Jay.

Jay's blue eyes darkened. "If I ever learn enough Latin and Greek. I'd rather be a farmer."

"You'll get to college, I'm sure," Sam Adams told him. "Come to see me when you do. The river ferry costs only a penny. Now I must get back to my writing."

The boys left with a copy of the four-sheet newspaper. They promised not to say they had seen Adams at the printer's shop.

The next day Sam and Ned Quincy came to see Johnny and Jay. They found the boys in the stables, brushing Imp and the colt that Johnny had ridden up from Braintree.

"Guess what's happened!" the Quincy boys said excitedly. "We bet you can't guess."

"You found a three-legged cat, or a bag of gold." Johnny grinned at them.

"That's right! What luck! You'd never believe it!" Sam said.

"Which is it?" Jay laughed.

"Gold, simple! You know the 'Bethel,' the ship Father and Uncle Ed Quincy own? Well, it captured a Spanish treasure ship, the 'Jesu, Maria,' with a cargo of silver and gold. We're rich!"

"How did it happen? How could such a small ship capture a big Spanish ship."

"I'll tell it. I'm the oldest," Ned said to Sam. "It happened at dusk. The 'Bethel' was going through the Straits of Gibralter. Suddenly it saw the 'Jesu, Maria's' lights. The 'Bethel' was too small to get away. So guess what our captain did," Ned added.

"What?" Johnny was wide-eyed.

"He hung lanterns high in the rigging. The crew fixed sticks with hats and coats on them to look like men. They set these along the rails. Then our captain bore down full sail on the 'Jesu, Maria' and demanded that it surrender."

"And he fooled the Spanish?"

Ned smiled. "Yes, in the dusk the Spanish captain thought our ship was a British war sloop. He surrendered without a shot."

"It's hard to believe, but wonderful!" Johnny said. "How many men did the Spanish have?"

120

"One hundred and ten men and twenty-six guns. And the 'Bethel' had only thirty-seven men and fourteen guns," Sam said proudly. He was about ready to burst.

Johnny gave Imp a slap on the flank with his brush. "First the French and now the Spanish," he said. "I tell you, New England men can beat anybody!" He chuckled happily.

"Father and Uncle Ed might sell their shipbuilding business," Sam went on. "They want to move back to Braintree."

"I'd hate to see you go. We'd miss you at school and all——"

"Oh, we don't know how soon," Sam replied easily. "We'll finish school here, I think. I'll follow Ned to college at Cambridge. That is, if I pass the entrance examinations."

The boys all rolled their eyes. They'd already learned that in taking the examinations one must answer all questions in Latin and Greek.

All too soon Jay's week in Boston passed. He had to return home to school. The three weeks in August were the only summer vacation the boys had.

Jay had ridden his colt up to town with a neighbor who had brought in a load of vegetables. Although Uncle Tom didn't like it, Jay insisted on riding the ten miles back alone.

"I'm almost thirteen," he exclaimed. "I'm old enough to find my way home."

The coachman fastened Jay's box behind his saddle. The saddle bags were stuffed with gifts for his family from the Hancocks. Prince and Johnny rode with him as far as the city gates.

Jay gave a last wave and trotted off.

Johnny put his fingers to his mouth and whistled shrilly. "Greet Little Turtle for me if you see him fishing. Tell him to be a good Indian."

Jay laughed. Then he kicked his colt's sides and galloped away.

Snowballs and Paul Revere

ONE AFTERNOON late in the year 1748, Uncle Thomas stamped into his front hall. He dropped his news-sheet, the "Independent Advertiser," on a marble table.

Cato took his gold cane. Then he brushed the snow off Uncle Thomas's gold-laced hat and cloak and put them away.

Johnny came down the curved stairway for tea.

"Lydia!" Uncle Tom shouted. "And you, Johnny! Come into the library." His double chins shook. Johnny had never seen him so angry.

Uncle Tom limped ahead. Johnny could tell that his gout hurt him.

Uncle Tom sat down slowly with a groan. "We have had bad news this day," he said. "England has returned Fort Louisburg in Canada to France! The treaty was signed in October. That's the thanks our heroes get for their capture of the gateway to the St. Lawrence River! It's all for nothing!"

Johnny and Aunt Lydia gasped. To think that England cared so little for the loss of American blood and money!

Aunt Lydia said sadly, "It's a shame! How do they dare? Is there nothing we can do?"

"Humph!" Uncle Tom snorted. "There's nothing we can do. It's done. But New England won't forget this. All our merchants are furious!"

"Tim O'Toole won't like it. Neither will any of the militia," Johnny spoke up.

"The militia say they won't fight for England again," Uncle Tom went on. "They're that angry. And why shouldn't they be? A treaty won't keep the French or their Indian allies from killing our western settlers."

Uncle Tom held up the little "Independent Advertiser." "Here's one news-sheet that's not afraid to speak up," he said. "You must both read it. The editor reminds England that our country, our Massachusetts, has lost seven thousand men, sick or dead. Many farms have gone to ruin. As a land-owner, I know that well!"

"Are you ready for tea?" Aunt Lydia reached for a silver bell.

"No! This writer even says that England doesn't care about us—that we should cut our ties with her. Hmmm. I wonder who dared to write this?"

"People say the names of the writers for that paper are kept secret," Aunt Lydia said.

Johnny felt a secret thrill of pleasure. He thought, "Sam Adams wrote that. At least someone dares to let England know what we think."

Near the end of December high snow drifts lined the streets. They filled the narrow lanes. The drifts were piled higher by the plows used to clear the streets. Harness bells jingled merrily as horses trotted along the streets pulling covered sleighs.

"Take this note over to Colonel Josiah Quincy's for me, Johnny," his aunt said one Saturday afternoon after school.

"Yes, ma'am." Johnny was pleased. He wanted to see Sam.

Soon he was on his way. His boots squeaked over the packed snow. He buried his mouth in the knitted scarf his mother had sent him.

Coming down the street were two older boys. They wore gray greatcoats, knit caps, and leather breeches. The bigger one carried a basket under his arm. They were laughing.

As they hurried past him, Johnny had a quick look in the basket. It was filled with snowballs!

"So!" Johnny thought. He turned his head. "The boys are gone. They must have slipped into that narrow lane I just passed."

He picked up some snow in his mittened hands and made a snowball. As he straightened up something whizzed past his head. Wham! Another snowball smacked against his back. He whirled around, but he could see no one.

Close by snow was drifted high against the front of a house. Johnny ran and dropped behind it. He waited.

Soon two heads peeked out of the lane. Then the two boys ran out to the street to look for their target.

Johnny jumped up. As fast as he could, he threw two snowballs. One missed, but the other hit the bigger boy full in the face. With a yell he slipped and fell to the street. Snowballs rolled helter-skelter from his basket.

Quick as a wink, Johnny ran back to the

smaller boy, who was trying to pick up the snow-balls. Johnny scooped up a chunk of snow and threw it over the boy's head.

"O-h-h, you——" the boy roared and grabbed Johnny. Johnny dodged away. At that moment the bigger boy got to his feet.

"I've seen him before," Johnny thought. "Now what's his name?"

The smaller boy took a step forward. He was grinning and wiping the snow from his face. "Let's get him, Paul."

Paul laughed. "We've met our match, Joe. And I know you," he said to Johnny. "You're the lucky fellow who lives in the grand house on Beacon Hill yonder. Your uncle comes to my father's shop. I'm Paul Revere and this is Joe."

Johnny smiled. "I thought I knew you. Do you still live near Clark's Wharf?"

"Aye, we do. I'm through North Writing School and learning to be a silversmith. I just

129

left a copper teakettle at a house down the street." Paul grinned. "And I don't like an empty basket," he added.

So that was why Johnny hadn't seen more of Paul Revere. The Reading and Writing Schools were for boys who would not go on to Harvard College but would become tradesmen. Many boys didn't even go to the Writing Schools.

Joe poked Paul. "Come on. We'll be late for bell practice at Old North."

"Old North" was what everyone in Boston called Christ's Church. Christ's Church was not a New England or Puritan church but an Episcopal or English church. It had a "royal peal" of bells that were said to be the sweetest and best bells in America. They could be heard in Cambridge clear across the Charles River. People even said their ringing had the power to chase away evil spirits!

"We've a club of bell-ringers," Paul told

Johnny. "Seven of us are paid for ringing the bells on Sundays and at other times, too. Since Christmas is day after tomorrow, we have to go over and practice now."

Christmas! Johnny was curious. No proper New England son noticed Christmas. The Puritans had thought it wicked to celebrate Christmas, and many New Englanders still thought so. Most of them, like Johnny's family, celebrated New Year's instead, with a school holiday and little gifts.

Johnny had heard how beautiful the Episcopal churches looked at Christmas-time. "I'd like to see Old North and hear you boys," he said. "Will you let me come, too?"

"Aye, come along. But it's a far walk."

When Paul and Joe pushed open the big doors of Christ's Church the wonderful smell of Christmas evergreens was everywhere.

Johnny looked at the church's carved altar, at

131

which candles were burning. He looked at the organ and the carved wooden statues, and his eyes grew wide. "How beautiful it is! So different from our plain church!" he said.

He saw several boys, their faces red from cold, hustle into the bell-tower. Paul followed them. Soon Johnny could hear the bell-ringer telling the boys how to ring a Christmas carol. When the music started, Johnny thought he could feel the ringing clear to his bones.

The New England Sabbath began at candle-lighting time on Saturday. So Johnny soon had to leave. Paul was still up in the bell-tower pulling hard at the bell ropes, but Johnny felt that **he had** made a new friend.

Johnny Goes to Cambridge

THE DAY was damp and misty. Johnny rode through the countryside with Aunt Lydia in their new yellow coach.

They were on their way to Cambridge and Harvard College. Johnny was to take his entrance examinations there, this July of 1750.

It would have been shorter to go by ferry across the Charles River. But the flat raft used as a ferry was unsafe for Aunt Lydia and the big coach.

Johnny shifted uneasily on the scarlet cushions. How he wished Uncle Tom hadn't been kept at home with his gout!

"What will the other fellows think," he wondered, "about my coming to the college with a coach and an aunt?"

He sighed. "If only Sam Quincy could have come today instead of tomorrow!"

He scratched his head. His wig itched. Now that he was thirteen and soon to be in college, Aunt Lydia said he must be in fashion. He had to wear a wig.

"Don't fidget so!" Aunt Lydia said.

"Yes, ma'am." He had been told what to expect today by Ned Quincy, who was already going to college. Four tutors and President Holyoke of Harvard would ask him questions. The questions would be in Latin and he must answer in Latin. Then he must change English into Latin and Greek.

He had his head out the open window as the coach neared Cambridge Common. The College faced the Common. A fence enclosed the College's three long brick buildings, which surrounded a square of land called the "yard." This yard was bare except for a large elm tree.

The coach stopped in front of a building. "Here's Harvard Hall, where I'm to report, Auntie," Johnny said.

Across from Harvard Hall to Johnny's right was Massachusetts Hall. It had a big clock on top. Stoughton Hall stood at the back of the square between the other halls.

"I'll rest at the inn," Aunt Lydia said. "Don't fret. You'll do well, John."

Johnny gave her a smile, although he felt shaky inside. "Yes, ma'am, I'll try."

He went in alone. About fifteen boys were sitting on benches, awaiting their turns. Some looked very young and frightened. Others tried not to look uneasy. They seemed to be from twelve to eighteen years of age.

When his turn came, Johnny walked into a

room paneled in wood. The President stood by a desk, wearing a black silk gown and a white bib collar. He bowed and so did Johnny.

"Ah! It's—ah—John Hancock?" He looked at the list on his desk. "I know your uncle. He's been most kind to our college."

"Yes, sir." Johnny let out his breath.

Then two teachers in black gowns and white wigs stepped forward and began to ask questions in Latin. Finally one of them gave Johnny a paper written in English. "Change this into Latin. You may use the study next door."

Johnny didn't learn how well he did in his work, but he was told later to make a copy of the college laws. Then he was told to bring his copy of the laws with him in August and he would be entered as a freshman.

Aunt Lydia was delighted. "I knew you could do it! Now we must return to Boston at once. If your uncle's gout improves, we shall come back for Commencement Day next week. Would you like that, John?"

"Wonderful!" Johnny said. "Aunt Lydia, I feel so much better, now that it's over. I could dance a jig!"

The Hancocks almost always came to Cambridge for Commencement Day. That was the day on which seniors were graduated from college. Held the second week in July, it was the biggest holiday in Massachusetts. Everyone in the colony was proud of Harvard College.

Shops in Boston closed tight and the townspeople went to Cambridge by the hundreds. Farmers and villagers from near and far gathered there, too.

Booths for food and drink and games dotted the Common. People slept on the Common in tents or wherever they could find a place. The four roads leading into town were a cloud of dust. Excited children ran everywhere.

Happily, Uncle Thomas was well enough to go to Cambridge the next week. The Hancocks came in their best satins and brocades. Uncle Tom sported gold buttons and gold shoe buckles. Aunt Lydia's hoop skirt was so large that Johnny and his uncle barely could squeeze into the big yellow coach.

At eleven o'clock Johnny stood outside the Meeting House. He felt warm in his peach-colored satin coat and blue satin breeches.

The church bell began to ring. Then he heard fifes and music. "Here they come!" people gathered before the church murmured.

Johnny watched in awe as all the students marched into the church. After them came President Holyoke, then the Royal Governor and other important people. All were dressed in bright silks and velvets or red and gold uniforms.

"You and your uncle have been given front row seats," Aunt Lydia whispered as she and

Johnny and Uncle Tom pushed through the crowd into the church.

Johnny could see that she was pleased. She went happily upstairs to sit with the other ladies in the balcony.

After many speeches, the black-robed seniors were given their "Bachelor of Arts" degrees. "Will I ever learn enough to win one, too?" Johnny wondered.

He glanced back at Sam Quincy, who sat in the row behind him. Sam looked back solemnly, then slowly winked.

Johnny almost giggled. "If Sam isn't worried, why should I be?" He sat back and waited for the end of the program. Then he could enjoy the acrobats and dancing on the Common and the dinner that would follow.

"Another month and I'll be part of all this!" he thought.

Harvard College and a Great Loss

"FRESHMAN Hancock! Oh, Hancock!" Thirteen-year-old Johnny felt someone shaking him.

"What? What?" He sat up in his narrow bed and rubbed his eyes.

A Harvard sophomore, a second-year man, stood over him. He wore a black gown with a plaid lining and held a fuzzy wig in his hands. "Take this over to the barber's to be curled before breakfast," he ordered.

"Before breakfast?" Johnny was dismayed. That meant he wouldn't have time to eat at the Buttery. All the college students snatched a bite of biscuit and milk there. "Yes, sir," he groaned.

140

He watched the sophomore strut out of the room with a pleased smile.

Johnny was a new Harvard student. He was bound not only by the school rules but also by the class rules. A freshman had to obey every upper classman.

His day started with church at six in the morning. At 6:30 he went to his first class. After that came breakfast, then more classes.

He ate dinner in the "Commons," a large eating hall. He washed his meat and vegetables down with cider. The cider was passed from person to person in two huge pewter mugs, which were scoured only once a week.

His afternoons from two o'clock until supper Johnny spent in study. After a supper of meat pie or bread and milk he studied in his room.

"This isn't the exciting life I'd thought it would be," Johnny said to Sam Quincy as they settled down for an evening's reading.

141

The next year Jay Adams arrived at Harvard. Johnny in turn awoke him early one morning. "Take my bob wig to the barber's, Jay, old fellow," he said without a smile. "Have it cleaned and curled right away."

He had to laugh at the look of dismay on Jay's face. "Remember," he added as he left the tiny room, "you can't wear your hat until you're a sophomore, Mr. Adams!"

In December of that year he was called to Lexington, for Grandfather Hancock had suddenly died. Johnny hired a horse at the stables and galloped over the snow-covered roads.

At the parsonage he greeted his family. His mother had come with her husband, Parson Daniel Perkins. Sister Mary was there, too, and schoolboy Ebenezer. Parson Perkins's son, Richard, had eyes for no one but sister Mary.

"How tall you've grown this past year," Mother said. She patted Johnny proudly.

"So handsome, too," Mary teased.

Johnny stood up and made a deep bow. "Thank you, ladies," he said jokingly, but his thin cheeks turned red.

"John is a good student at Harvard," Uncle Tom said proudly. "He will be a help to me in my business."

After the funeral Johnny returned to school. For the next two years he continued to study Latin, Greek, religion, and famous English writers. In his fourth and last year he studied arithmetic, geometry, and geography.

Just before he finished college his sister Mary married Richard Perkins. Then all the family came to Cambridge on July 17, 1754, to enjoy Johnny's graduation. He was seventeen.

Uncle Tom took Johnny into his business at once as a clerk. He had a desk by a window looking out on the docks. Around the corner was the noisy market square.

"Rattle, thump, rum-te-tum!" Johnny muttered as he dipped his quill pen into his inkhorn one day. "How can anyone think?"

He was making copies of all the business orders which Uncle Tom sent to England and Europe. These copies were kept in a "letter book." Often several copies of a letter were sent on different ships. Sometimes ships were lost or captured during a war.

"Whatever became of your clerk, Tim O'Toole?" Johnny asked his uncle one day. "I thought he was your best clerk."

"Aye, so he was. But he wanted to start his own shop, so I helped him to do it. He's getting along fine, too."

"I'm glad to hear it. I must call on him. You were always good about helping young men in business, Uncle Tom."

During the next few years Johnny worked hard to learn the vast Hancock business. Uncle

144

Tom had spells of gout, and the work fell more and more on Johnny's shoulders.

A letter from Grandmother Hancock brought good news. Johnny's cousin, Lucy Bowes, had married Parson Jonas Clark. He had become pastor at Lexington after Grandfather's death. Lucy and her family were moving into the Lexington parsonage and would keep Grandmother company. Johnny and his aunt and uncle drove out often to see them.

War with France was brewing again, for France wanted the Ohio River country. Uncle Tom got orders to supply the British troops in the colonies. His ships began to collect army supplies from England and various places along the coast. Soon England declared war on France.

One night Uncle Tom brought home a young army officer from Virginia. He was taller than Johnny and had merry blue eyes and powdered, reddish hair.

"This is Major George Washington," Uncle Tom said. "He fought with General Braddock out in the Ohio country."

"It's an honor to meet you, Major," nineteen-year-old Johnny said with a bow. He felt honored indeed. Major Washington had had two horses shot from under him during the fight. If it had not been for him, Braddock's defeat by the French and Indians would have been even worse.

The young Major told Johnny that he had come to talk to the Massachusetts Governor about fighting the French. "The British must learn to fight from behind trees as the Indians do," he said. "Then we can win."

"Heh, I'll see that the Governor heeds that advice, young man," Uncle Tom said with a nod. "We have to protect our settlers, and we must take Fort Louisburg again."

Two years later, in 1758, Fort Louisburg was recaptured. Then, on a bright September day,

General Amherst and his four thousand troops returned to Boston and camped on the Common. All Boston welcomed them.

"This time we'll keep Fort Louisburg," everyone said happily. "The St. Lawrence River is open. France's power in America is broken."

The next morning Johnny came down the stone steps of his house. He heard drums and fifes sounding briskly over the Common.

"I want to go to the British Coffee House for dinner this noon," he told Uncle Tom. "I'd like to hear firsthand about the capture of Louisburg. Surely some of the officers will be there today."

"Aye, John, go along," Uncle Tom said. "I have government business at the Town House. Be sure to ask after Lieutenant Tim O'Toole."

That noon Johnny sat at a table in the crowded inn and talked to several young officers. "Didn't you know Lieutenant Timothy O'Toole?" he said to one officer he knew.

148

The young man looked sad. "Yes, I knew him. He was killed, I'm sorry to say."

"Killed!" Johnny was shocked. He wet his lips and swallowed hard. "This is terrible news. I knew him a long time ago."

"He went out with a patrol of scouts. There was an Indian along by the name of Little Turtle. They were caught by a French patrol, but they gave warning in time for the rest of our patrol to escape."

"Little Turtle, too!" Johnny shook his head. How odd that two friends from childhood should die together! His eyes grew dim and he pushed away his pewter plate.

"If only England hadn't been so stupid and given Fort Louisburg back to the French that first time!" he said bitterly. "My friends might not have had to die now."

The British officers frowned, but Johnny didn't care. He didn't even notice them.

John Fights the Stamp

JOHNNY KNOCKED at Uncle Tom's front bedroom door. Cato opened it.

"Heh, John, come in, come in," Uncle Tom ordered from his big four-posted bed.

Johnny looked at his uncle's swollen legs. "Is your gout better? I was much hurried today and couldn't come sooner."

"Aye, I know. I'm sorry I've been ill these past few months. I'm glad I had your help as a business partner. John, I've decided to build our own ships to carry whale oil to England. I want you to build a fast little packet that will make the voyage as quickly as possible."

"Whale oil is scarce and the price is high," Johnny said. "We'll make a good profit. I'll see to it at once, sir."

By 1764, three Hancock-owned packets, the "British Packet," the "Lydia," and the "Harrison," sped back and forth across the ocean.

These little merchant ships could cross the ocean in the fast time of three or four weeks. They carried whale oil, whale bone, tar, and wood staves to London. They brought back Irish butter, pork and manufactured goods.

One August noon Cato rushed into John's office. "Come quick. Mister Thomas, he sick. He have heart attack at Town House."

"Heaven save him!" John gasped. He knew that his uncle had planned to go to a meeting of the Governor's Council. He dropped his quill and rushed home. Uncle Thomas died that afternoon.

With his uncle's death, John became the richest man in New England and the second richest in America. His uncle left him about 80,000 pounds in English money.

John's brother Ebenezer was left some money, too. "I'm going to open my own hardware store," he told John.

John looked doubtful. "These are hard times," he said, "but I'll help you."

Smallpox had struck Boston. Shops were closed. People fled the town. There was no work. Ships stood empty in the harbor.

Then came some startling news. England needed money and her Parliament placed a new tax on American business. It was called a stamp tax. Every piece of business paper and every newspaper must have a tax stamp on it.

The colonists were indignant. "We had no voice in saying what kind of tax we should pay," they said. "England has no right to tax us without our consent. She's taking away our liberty."

John couldn't believe that the King would agree to the tax, but he did. It would start on November 1, 1765.

John wrote angry letters against the tax to his merchant friends in England. "This Stamp Tax is very cruel. It will ruin American trade and the country," he said.

He was so angry that he joined a club of patriots at Sam Adams' invitation. Sam was a poor business man, but he was good at politics.

The Long Room Club met above the printing office of the "Boston Gazette." Jay Adams, now a lawyer, was also a member. He and Sam wrote against the Stamp Tax in the four-page newspaper. Paul Revere, now a famous silversmith, met with them. Another member was a handsome, blond young doctor named Joseph Warren.

The feeling against the Stamp Tax grew hotter with the weather. One August day a stuffed dummy of an officer of the colony was hanged in

153

a large elm tree on the south side of town. A crowd soon gathered and carried the dummy down to the Town House in King Street. The Governor and his Council were meeting there. The crowd tore down a shack on a dock that was to have been the Stamp Tax office. Then, with cheers and yells, they burned the dummy.

Two weeks later John and Aunt Lydia were sitting in their summer house. They were trying to find a breeze in the hot night. John told his aunt about his new ship. "I'll call her the 'Liberty.' She'll soon be ready to sail—before the Stamp Tax starts," he added.

Cato rushed out to them. "The mob's out again in North Boston," he cried. "Oh, Mister John, they tearing down the Lieutenant-governor's house. They mad at him."

"Cato, take a lantern and follow the crowd. Report back to me in an hour," John ordered.

Cato began to shake. "In the dark? I scared,"

he said. "I afraid that old Mister Stamp Act catch me."

John had to smile. "It won't, Cato, but never mind about going."

"Do something, John!" Aunt Lydia cried.

John frowned and shook his head. "What can I do against a mob? Still, it's wrong to destroy property. It's not 'liberty' to run wild. Sam Adams must take these people in hand."

The Lieutenant-governor's house, furniture, and garden were hacked to pieces. All Boston was ashamed of the act, and the mob leaders were arrested.

During the following winter John wrote to his English merchant friends. "I will do no business under the stamp," he said. "I will not subject myself to slavery."

He persuaded other American traders to agree to do no business with English merchants. This brought the Stamp Act to an end.

In May John was pleased to be elected as a representative to the General Court.

A few days later his brig "Harrison" brought the official report of the repeal of the Stamp Act. "I'll send this news to the Governor and his Council at once," John said proudly.

Boston set aside a day to celebrate the victory. John talked over his plans for the celebration with his friends in the Long Room Club. "Now that I am a member of the General Court," he said, "I think I should give the public a show of fireworks."

Church bells began ringing before dawn on the day of the celebration. During the day bands played, militia paraded, and guns boomed. Flags covered all the houses.

That night Sam Adams' Sons of Liberty shot off fireworks on the Common. John answered with his own fireworks from a platform in front of his house. He opened his house to the public.

"We can hope for peace now," John told Aunt Lydia after the last guest had gone.

The next winter a great fire swept the houses along Boston's waterfront. "I'll help these homeless people," John thought.

He gave a large sum of money for them. Every winter he gave huge stacks of firewood to the needy. Boston loved him for this.

Aunt Lydia was pleased when he opened his large iron chest of silver coins for the churches.

157

He bought glass windows, pews, bells, and Bibles for them.

One day John met Sam Adams walking along with the town sheriff.

"What's the meaning of this, Sam? Where are you going?" he asked.

"I'm going to jail for my debts," Sam said with a sad smile. "I can't pay them."

"We can't have this," John said sharply. "I will give you the money. We need you if ever we have to fight again for our rights."

Many times in the next few years John's money helped in the struggle for liberty. His hope for no more trouble with England did not come true. England passed another tax on business and sent more men to collect it.

One day John went to a meeting of the General Court. He stood up before the group and said angrily, "No customs tax collector shall board my ships. I won't pay this unfair tax."

Salt-Water Tea

JOHN WAS able to keep his vow in the spring of 1768. Late one day he and a clerk stood on the Clark-Hancock Wharf watching his ship "Liberty" being loaded. Barrels of whale oil brought in by John's eight whaling ships were hoisted on board the "Liberty."

John looked at the British man-o'-war "Romney" out in the harbor. "I'm in a hurry to get the 'Liberty' under way. She'll have to sail tonight," he said.

His clerk nodded. " 'Tis a wonder nothing has happened since you wouldn't pay the tax on the cargo she brought from Spain. You're the first merchant to defy the customs tax collectors. Something's up with the 'Romney' here."

Something was up. John had hardly reached home when the clerk galloped up Beacon Hill on a borrowed horse. He was so excited he could hardly talk.

"The 'Romney' is taking the 'Liberty'!" he shouted. "Two tax collectors came to seize her because you didn't pay your customs tax. A crowd of sailors and shipbuilders fought them off, but two boats of British sailors took her over. She's being towed to the 'Romney'!"

John's heart sank. By the time he reached the dock the crowd was gone. He stood with his captain and watched the "Liberty" made fast under the guns of the "Romney."

"Sir, she's a total loss if the British don't return her," the clerk said sadly.

"I heard the tax collectors say you're to be arrested," the captain said.

160

"By Heaven, I'm ready to lose much in this fight for our rights!" John said angrily. "I'll hire a good lawyer to defend me."

Should he ask John Adams or Sam Quincy, both fine lawyers? He remembered that Sam seemed to favor the King's side in these matters. He would ask John Adams.

He rode home later. He noticed smoke rising from the Common against the darkening sky. A crowd was gathered around a bonfire there.

Aunt Lydia and the servants clustered on the porch. "They've taken a taxman's boat and burned it," Aunt Lydia said anxiously.

John told her what had happened to his ship. "There's no telling where this will end. But I shall fight them."

The British officials brought John into court. John Adams defended him well. No one would speak against him, because the people admired him for standing up for their rights. At last the

161

government dropped its case against him, but his ship was not returned.

By fall there were four thousand British soldiers and six warships in Boston. The townspeople hated the red-coated troops.

"Why should we pay for soldiers to guard us like enemies?" they said.

Secret patriot clubs met to plan ways of getting rid of the troops. By spring feelings had risen to the danger point.

One March night in 1770 a British soldier was standing guard near the British barracks in King Street. A crowd gathered in the moonlight to jeer. "Lobsters! Bloody-backs!" they shouted, and threw clam shells and chunks of ice at him.

The sentry struck at a boy. Angered, the crowd pressed forward.

"Turn out the main guard!" the sentry shouted.

At once eight soldiers and an officer, Captain Preston, ran from the barracks. They stood in

front of the sentry. The crowd closed in, scream-
ing, "Shoot us if you dare!"

Suddenly there was a scuffle. Somebody cried,
"Fire!" Eight muskets cracked, and five persons
fell dead or dying to the snow.

Silently the crowd carried the dead and
wounded away, but it was not long before the
town was in an uproar.

The next day John and Sam Adams went with
a committee to call on the Governor. They asked
him to send the soldiers away before more trouble arose. The Governor was forced to agree.

The patriots began to call this event the "Boston Massacre." They did not forget it.

Several years passed quietly after the troops
left. John was able to spend more time on his
business. England removed the taxes and duties
that had angered the American people.

One day Aunt Lydia brought home a young
relative to stay with her. Her name was Dolly

Quincy. She was a cousin of Sam and Ned Quincy. John had not seen her in several years.

"Dolly Quincy! That little girl?" he exclaimed when Aunt Lydia first told him that Dolly was coming to live with them.

"I've promised her father, Squire Edmund, to look after her," Aunt Lydia said. "I've felt sorry for the poor man since his wife died. He has such a big family! Dolly is very pretty." She smiled at John.

Aunt Lydia and Dolly often made visits to the homes of friends and relatives near Boston. John found himself glad to go, too, if his gout was not bothering him.

Suddenly England thought of a new plan to raise taxes and to get rid of her tea at the same time. John explained the plan to Dolly.

"England will sell tea cheaply to certain American merchants who are loyal to her. No one else can sell it. I won't get any, of course!"

Once more Americans rose up in arms. On every side John heard people say, "We'll neither buy nor drink the tea. We will not be taxed without our consent."

In December, 1773, three British ships, the "Dartmouth," the "Beaver," and the "Eleanor," reached Boston. Each ship carried 114 chests of tea. It was cheap tea, but it still carried the hated tax.

The people of Boston would not buy the tea or let it land. Governor Hutchinson would not permit the ships to leave the harbor, either. Patriot groups stood guard to keep the tea from being unloaded.

The patriot leaders called a meeting of all the people for December 16.

On that day, as Colonel of the Independent Company of Cadets, John marched down to Griffin's Wharf with some of his cadets. He saluted Paul Revere, who was on guard duty.

165

"We'll relieve you and the other guards now, Revere," he said. "Another group is coming to relieve me later, before the meeting at Old South Church."

Paul shouldered his musket. "There's no use waiting on Governor Hutchinson to act. He won't let the ships sail back to England unless we pay the tax on the tea. We might as well go ahead with the plans we made at the Green Dragon Tavern the other night."

John smiled. "We'll know this day," he said.

Two thousand people crowded into and around Old South Church. They didn't mind the rainy day. They were all waiting for a message from the Governor.

Sam Adams talked to the crowd. Then Dr. Joseph Warren and John talked to them. Excitement rose. What should be done if the Governor and the British soldiers out on Fort Castle Island kept the ships in harbor?

166

At last the messenger returned from his long trip to the Governor, who was staying out of town. It was almost six o'clock. Candles were burning in the church. The messenger repeated what the Governor had said. Unless the tea tax was paid he would not allow the tea ships to sail back to England.

At once yells arose. "To Griffin's Wharf!" "Mohawks, out!" "Salt-water tea tonight!"

Then John heard himself shouting above the hubbub, "Let every man do what is right in his own eyes!"

Soon dark figures crept from the Green Dragon Tavern. They were wrapped in blankets and their faces were dark with soot and red paint.

More figures met them. Then, over 150 strong, they marched two by two through the darkness toward Griffin's Wharf.

John and Sam Adams followed and lost themselves in the large crowd gathered at the wharf.

Along with the others, they watched the Mohawks row out and climb aboard the tea ships. The ships' crews dared not stand in their way.

John saw the Mohawks hoist the tea chests on deck. He heard axes crack the chests open. He saw the Mohawks dump the tea into the sea!

Soon tea covered the shore for miles. "How many cups of salt-water tea are being made tonight?" John wondered. "And what will England do to Massachusetts now?"

"New York and Philadelphia must know what Boston has done," he told the other patriot leaders later. "Will they stand by us?" So Paul Revere was sent to find out.

England did her worst. She closed the port of Boston on June 1, 1774. There would be no work and no food for these dangerous people, she said, until they paid the tax on the tea.

England sent General Thomas Gage to be the new Governor of Massachusetts. Soon after him more warships and four thousand more soldiers were sent to Boston.

John met Governor Gage at the dock with his Independent Company of Cadets. They were dressed in the gay uniforms that he had paid for.

One of Governor Gage's first acts was to close the Massachusetts General Court. "We'll keep on meeting," the representatives vowed. After that they called themselves the Provincial Congress of Massachusetts and moved from town to town to escape arrest.

By now Boston swarmed with soldiers. One day merchants loyal to the King came to John. "It's being said General Gage has secret orders to arrest you and Sam Adams for treason," they warned. "You'll be sent to England and hanged."

John stood straight and tall. "You know," he said, "I'll be willing to spend my fortune and my life in so good a cause."

But General Gage waited.

One morning in March, 1775, John was awakened by the sound of music. British soldiers marching on the Common were singing a new song.

> "Yankee Doodle came to town,
> For to buy a firelock.
> We will tar and feather him,
> And so we will John Hancock."

John burst out laughing. "Tar and feathers for me? I'll not be in Boston a day longer."

He rang for Cato. "Is my boat ready to cross the river? My aunt and Mistress Dolly will drive to Lexington later in the coach. I'll meet them there at the parsonage."

"Yes, Mister John, it's ready," Cato said.

John was going to Concord, where the Provincial Congress was meeting. Then he would go to Philadelphia as a delegate to the Second Continental Congress.

Let the British soldiers try to catch him!

A Midnight Warning

AT MIDNIGHT on April 18 a horseman galloped past Lexington Green. He sped up Bedford Turnpike to the Clark-Hancock parsonage.

A group of Minute Men stood guard around the frame house. They called out, "Halt!"

John, resting upstairs, heard the rider cry, "I want to see John Hancock and Sam Adams."

"Not so much noise," said Sergeant Will Monroe. "You'll awaken the whole family."

"Noise!" said the rider. "You'll have noise enough before long. The Regulars are coming!"

Windows were raised. Both Parson Clark and John stuck their heads out.

John saw Paul Revere standing in the cold moonlight. "Come in, Revere. We are not afraid of you," he said.

Quickly Paul Revere gave his message. "Dr. Warren sent me and Will Dawes to warn you and all the countryside," he said. "The British Regulars are marching from Boston. They are to arrest you and Sam Adams and capture our store of powder and supplies at Concord."

"We must leave at once," Sam Adams said.

John went to the door in his silk dressing gown. "Ring the church bell for the alarm," he told the Minute Men.

By now Cousin Lucy Bowes Clark and the Clark children, Aunt Lydia and Dolly Quincy had all come down to hear the news, too.

John began to clean his sword and pistol. He was determined to stay and fight the British. His aunt and Dolly begged him to leave.

Soon Will Dawes arrived. The two messengers

had something to eat, then rode off toward Concord to spread the alarm.

Later in the night a tired Paul Revere stumbled into the parsonage. "I was captured by several British officers," he reported. "They took my good horse. After a while they let me go, just outside this village. I walked back. Will Dawes escaped and went on."

By now it was almost dawn. The church bell was still ringing, *ding, dong, dong*. The rattle and roll of a drum brought the militia to the Green. Word came that six companies of British Regulars were almost at hand.

Finally John put on his scarlet cloak. He climbed into his carriage along with Sam and Paul. "If I had my musket, I would never turn my back on these troops," he said.

They drove to a house only two miles away in Woburn village. Then John sent Paul back to Lexington. "I've left a leather trunk at Buckman's Tavern," he said. "Do you think you can get it? It's full of important papers of our Provincial Congress and must not be lost."

Later John learned that Paul carried the trunk through the seventy-seven farmers drawn up on the Green. Just after Paul had reached the road he heard the first shots of the Revolution.

John heard the distant shots, too. "It's begun," he said. "I wonder what's happening."

He and Sam Adams moved from place to place to hide from the British soldiers. Then they started south to the Continental Congress at Philadelphia. All along the way, they and other delegates were led into the towns by large crowds of people and companies of militia.

Philadelphia was the largest and richest town in America. John looked with interest at its neat brick houses and tree-lined streets.

The first day he walked to the State House on Chestnut Street with John Adams and the other delegates. Old friends greeted one another in a beautiful, white-paneled room with two large fireplaces.

Ben Franklin arrived in his brown Quaker coat. George Washington came from Virginia in an elegant blue and buff uniform and a sword. Soon he would be offered the command of the thousands of militia that had gathered outside the city of Boston.

"Let us make John Hancock President of Congress," the delegates said to one another. "He's one of the first to oppose King George. He's a great leader. Without his help the Boston patriots could not have held out."

John was surprised and pleased. His friend Benjamin Harrison of Virginia placed him in the President's chair. "We will show Britain how much we think of her making you an outlaw," he said heartily.

At once John was swallowed up in work. As

176

the leader of Congress he had to plan a war. He begged supplies from the colonies. They were jealous of one another and slow to send men or money. John's pen was busy scratching out orders and letters.

In August Congress took a short rest. John hurried to Fairfield, Connecticut, where Aunt Lydia and Dolly were staying. Then, dressed in a crimson velvet suit, he took dark-eyed Dolly Quincy as his bride. After the wedding they stepped into the yellow Hancock coach to return to Philadelphia.

"Good-by, Aunt Lydia." Dolly waved her ivory fan. Aunt Lydia, tall and dignified, waved happily back.

John never saw his Aunt Lydia again. She died soon afterward.

The British troops held Boston. Congress talked about burning the town to drive them away. John owned many houses there, but he

178

wrote to General Washington: "If you must burn Boston, I heartily wish it. Even though I may suffer the greatest loss."

He was deep in planning a navy, too. Congress ordered thirteen ships to be built and made John chairman of the Marine Committee.

Still more letters flowed from John's pen. He urged all colonists to change merchant ships into warships. Massachusetts built two war frigates, the "Hancock" and the "Boston."

One day in March, 1776, an express rider brought a letter to John from General Washington. "The British have left Boston!" the General wrote. It was an American victory.

John and the other delegates to Congress were happy about the good news. "This shows what I've always known," John said proudly. "We Americans can take care of ourselves."

Washington wrote that British generals had lived in John's Beacon Hill house. Small harm had come to it. The stables and coach houses had been turned into hospitals. But his store on Anne Street had been burned.

A thousand Loyalists had sailed away from Boston with General Howe's fleet. Among them was Sam Quincy. John's heart was sad. "How many old friends are parted by this war," he said.

Dolly was indignant. "To think that my cousin would leave his own country!" she said with a toss of her brown head. "It's a disgrace to all the Quincys."

John wrote more letters. "We need more help with the war. It is near a turning point. Our militia must decide one question. Will they live slaves, or die free men?"

Another great question faced Congress, too. John talked about it to Thomas Jefferson, John and Sam Adams. "The time has come to act," he said. "Congress must decide. Should the colonies declare themselves a free nation?"

180

Signer for Independence

THE AFTERNOON of Thursday, July 4, 1776, was hot. The tired delegates of the Continental Congress gathered in the State House in Philadelphia stopped talking. Some of them moved closer to John Hancock, who was standing at a mahogany table in the front of the room. They held their breaths and watched. For John was reading a hand-written paper lying on the table.

"Will he dare sign the paper alone?" one delegate whispered to another. "If the Revolution fails, he'll be called a traitor. England will hang him, surely."

"He's a brave man," the other delegate re-

181

plied. "He'll sign. Anyhow, he's already been called a traitor and threatened with hanging."

John drew a pen from the silver inkstand on the table. Then, leaning forward, he signed his name in a beautiful hand.

"It's done!" he said aloud. "As President of Congress, I have signed America's Declaration of Independence from England!"

Then he added, "We shall have this printed right away. This Declaration will be sent to our armies and to every town in America."

A few days later he stood in the State House yard. He heard the Declaration read to the public for the first time.

"Huzzah for the United States! Huzzah for

Congress and John Hancock! Now we are free!" the crowd shouted.

John's heart swelled with pride. "But we still have to fight hard for that freedom," he told the crowd. "We must never give up."

All the new states celebrated the joyful news. They had parades and burned bonfires.

John's name was the only one on the first printed copy of the Declaration. Congress ordered a beautiful parchment copy to be made.

On this parchment fifty members of Congress signed their names on August 2. Again John signed first in his large, bold hand.

"There!" he said. He handed the quill to the next delegate. "England can read my name without glasses. She may now double her reward for my head."

He turned to Benjamin Franklin. "There must be no pulling different ways," he said earnestly. "We must hang together."

Franklin nodded. His old eyes twinkled. "If we don't, we shall hang separately."

John smiled. He was ready to give up everything for his country.

Two years passed. John worked so hard that his health grew bad. The states quarreled among themselves. The small states were jealous of the large ones.

John smoothed out their quarrels. By his tact and skill he held Congress together. Yet he drove the new states to carry on the war. He wrote to them many times:

"If we will only stand firm, we will win. We will secure the independence, the happiness, and the glory of the United States of America."

At last his bad health made him decide to leave Congress. His friends were sorry to see him go.

"You have tried to make us think first of the war effort," they told him. "You have tried to

184

show us how to be real patriots. No one but you could have run Congress so well. Through all our bad times, you have given us heart and spirit."

General Washington loaned a dozen Light Horsemen to guard John on his journey home. When he and Dolly entered Boston, the people's cheers warmed their hearts.

His old Independent Company of Cadets paid him honor. Thirteen cannon shots boomed out from the ships in the harbor. The Hill Fort guns answered. All the city's bells rang.

Dolly gave John a proud smile. "They still love you. They know what you've done for them," she said.

Boston looked different. The fine trees and fences had been cut down for firewood by the English soldiers. So had old North Meeting House and the ancient waterfront buildings, and even the Liberty Tree. The people of Boston soon put up a Liberty Pole in its place.

185

John found that his house needed repairs. While these were being made, he added a large dining hall. Here he gave many gay dinners when he felt better.

In June of 1778 the German Baron Steuben arrived in Boston. "I'm on my way to headquarters at Valley Forge," he told John. "General Washington has asked me to train his troops."

They talked over his plans in John's comfortable library. "You'll need a good sum of money for this," John said. "I want to help."

He took the key to his iron money chest from the pocket of his velvet coat. He opened the chest and gave the Baron five thousand dollars in silver to help pay for the American soldiers' training.

The next year the tall square sails of a French fleet filled the harbor. Boston was angry with the French sailors. The fleet had failed in an attack on Newport, Rhode Island.

John was troubled. If the people of Boston made the French sail away, America would lose their badly needed help. So every day John fed some of the French officers. Often so many came that he ran short of food.

One summer morning Dolly and John looked out their door. The sun sparkled on the gold lace of over a hundred French uniforms. Their wearers were crossing the Common from their ship. They were coming to John's for breakfast.

"What shall I do?" gasped Dolly. "You said you had invited only thirty."

"I did! Send Harry to the neighbors to borrow turkeys and hams," John ordered.

Dolly looked at the cows that were grazing on the Common. Then she called her servants.

"Go milk every cow you can find," she told them. "We'll explain to their owners later."

The Frenchmen had a fine time at the breakfast. They decided to stay and help America.

One fall day John waited at home in a fine red velvet suit. Dolly patted her fashionable hairdress. "Isn't it past time?" she asked him. "You're so calm."

Lively band music sounded outside. Knocks thundered on the door. John smiled.

"The committee's here—to tell me I'm elected the first Governor of the State of Massachusetts!"

John Hancock's election was for one year. He was sworn in at the Town House, now called the State House. Everyone celebrated with parades and fine parties.

The exciting news of the British surrender at Yorktown, Virginia, came to John in 1781. Even though he was ill in bed with the gout, his happiness was complete. "I'm proud I had a part in the struggle for our glorious United States," he told Dolly.

That December General LaFayette strode into John's bedroom.

188

"Ah, my good friend!" John greeted him. "What brings you here?"

"I've come to tell you more about the battle at Yorktown last October. It means the war is over. We've won!"

John gave a sigh of relief, then smiled happily. "So I'd hoped. Now I feel my work is done. General, I've lost much money in this war. But by the smile of Heaven, I'm a free and independent man!"

John's work was not done yet. Nine times the people of Massachusetts elected him their Governor. He did much for them.

"He comes and talks to us as a brother," the dock workers would say. "He lighted our dark streets at night."

"He even gives us band music on the Common," young boys would say.

However, two great sorrows came to John and Dolly. They lost a baby daughter, and then they

190

lost their only son. He was a fine young boy whom they had named John George Washington Hancock, in honor of the General.

It soon became clear that the new little country needed a stronger union. Every state was asked to vote on a new Constitution. Many people in Massachusetts thought the Constitution was too powerful and did not want their state to agree to it.

John was chosen to preside over the meeting called to decide on the Constitution. In a speech to the delegates, he suggested several changes that would protect the peoples' rights. Only after these changes were adopted, would the Massachusetts delegates vote in favor of adopting the Constitution. Later, the same changes were agreed to by other states. They came to be known as America's "Bill of Rights."

The long war for independence had ruined Uncle Thomas Hancock's great trading business.

Now John gave all his time to being Governor. The people liked him.

His health grew steadily worse, however. The last time he spoke in the State House before his death he said, "'I think I have done my duty as a servant of the people. I never did and never will deceive them while I have life and strength to act in their service."

John Hancock gave his life, his name, and his fortune to help make the colonies a free nation. The people of New England loved him as a great patriot and leader.

John Adams, his old friend, called him "One of the firmest pillars of the Revolution."

More About This Book

WHEN JOHN HANCOCK LIVED

1737　JOHN HANCOCK WAS BORN IN BRAINTREE, NOW QUINCY, MASSACHUSETTS, JANUARY 23.

There were thirteen English colonies in America, ruled by King George II.

The population of the colonies was about 820,000.

1737–
1750　JOHN GREW UP IN BRAINTREE AND BOSTON, WHERE HE LIVED WITH HIS UNCLE.

The first magazine was published in North America, 1741.

The first scientific association was formed in America, 1743.

1750–
1764　JOHN ATTENDED HARVARD COLLEGE AND WORKED.

The French and Indian War began, 1754.

The French were defeated at the Battle of Quebec, 1759.

The French and Indian War ended, 1763.

1764–
1775

YOUNG HANCOCK INHERITED HIS UNCLE'S BUSINESS AND CONTINUED TO OPERATE IT.

The Stamp Act was passed, 1765, and repealed the following year.

The Boston Massacre occurred, 1770.

The "Boston Tea Party" took place, 1773.

The First Continental Congress met, 1774.

The first battle of the Revolutionary War was fought at Lexington, Massachusetts, 1775.

1775–
1777

HANCOCK WAS PRESIDENT OF THE SECOND CONTINENTAL CONGRESS.

The Second Continental Congress met, 1775.

The Declaration of Independence was signed, 1776.

General Burgoyne surrendered, 1777.

1777–
1783

HANCOCK WAS A POLITICAL LEADER AND BECAME GOVERNOR OF MASSACHUSETTS.

General Cornwallis surrendered at Yorktown, 1781.

Peace treaty with England was signed, ending the Revolutionary War, 1783.

The Constitutional Convention met to frame the Constitution of the United States, 1787.

194

1793   JOHN HANCOCK DIED IN BOSTON, OCTOBER 8.
There were thirteen states in the Union.

George Washington was President.

The population of the country was about
4,342,000.

DO YOU REMEMBER?

1. Where did Johnny Hancock live when he was a small boy?

2. What two boys did Johnny often play with when he was a boy?

3. What did Johnny and Mary do when they visited Uncle Tom in Boston?

4. Why did Johnny go to live in Boston with his uncle and aunt?

5. Why did the Governor of Massachusetts send a force to attack Fort Louisburg?

6. Where did Johnny go to school in Boston and what did he study?

7. How did Johnny and Aunt Lydia save a sailor from a British "press gang"?

8. What was Jay Adams' cousin, Sam, doing at the office of the "Independent Advertiser"?

9. What kind of entrance examination did Johnny take at college?

10. Where did Young Hancock start to work after he graduated from college?

11. What happened to Uncle Tom's merchandising business after he died?

12. Why were the people of Boston angry about the Stamp Tax?

13. What were the Boston Massacre and the Boston Tea Party?

14. What part did John Hancock play in the signing of the Declaration of Independence?

IT'S FUN TO LOOK UP THESE THINGS

1. What kind of government did Massachusetts have in colonial days?

2. What was the Continental Congress to which John Hancock belonged?

3. What goods did Boston merchants buy and sell before the Revolutionary War?

4. Who were the Sons of Liberty, and why were they organized?

5. How did Samuel Adams serve the colonists during the Revolutionary War period?

6. What other men of Boston were important leaders in John Hancock's time?

INTERESTING THINGS YOU CAN DO

1. Make a collection of pictures of old Boston for an exhibit on the bulletin board.

2. Prepare a report on colonial schools, such as the dame school and the Latin school.

3. Make a map showing the location of Beacon Hill, Cambridge, Bunker Hill, Breed's Hill, Charles River, and the waterfront.

4. Bring pictures to show how Boston men and women dressed about 1775.

5. Read to find out more about the "Boston Tea Party," and why it was held.

6. Read the famous poem "Paul Revere's Ride," written by Henry Wadsworth Longfellow.

OTHER BOOKS YOU MAY ENJOY READING

American Revolution, Bruce Lancaster. Doubleday.

Ben Franklin: Boy Printer, Augusta Stevenson. Trade and School Editions, Bobbs-Merrill.

Dawn at Lexington, N. W. James. Longmans.

Johnny Tremain, Esther Forbes. Houghton.

Our Independence and the Constitution, Dorothy Canfield Fisher. Trade Edition, Random House. School Edition, Hale.

Paul Revere: Boy of Old Boston, Augusta Stevenson. Trade and School Editions, Bobbs-Merrill.

INTERESTING WORDS IN THIS BOOK

apprentice (ă prĕn′tĭs) : young person, usually a boy, bound by agreement to work for another person for a certain period of time in order to learn an art or trade

barracks (băr′ăks) : building or buildings in which soldiers live

brocade (brȯ kād′) : cloth with a raised figure or design, usually woven of silk, gold, or silver threads

198

chaise (shāz) : covered carriage with two wheels, drawn by one horse

cipher (sī'fẽr) : use figures in arithmetic, as to add or subtract

cloak (clōk) : loose outer garment worn over regular clothing

foolscap (fōōlz'kăp') : sheets of writing paper

frigate (frĭg'ĭt) : medium-sized warship with three masts and square sails

Greek (grēk) : language spoken by the people of ancient Greece

Latin (lăt'ĭn) : language spoken by the people of ancient Rome

loft (lŏft) : attic, upper floor of a business building or warehouse

marine (má rēn') : pertaining to the sea

militia (mĭ lĭsh'á) : group of citizens organized as a military unit, but called into service only for emergency purposes

packet (păk'ĕt) : fast sailing boat, usually small and having fixed sailing dates for carrying mail, passengers, and goods

parchment (pärch'mĕnt) : skin of a sheep or other animal, prepared for writing purposes

199

pewter (pū'tẽr) : alloy or mixture of tin and some other metal, used for making utensils

plaid (plăd) : square piece of cloth with a checked pattern, worn about the shoulders

plummet (plŭm'ĕt) : small piece of lead used as a weight or writing instrument

portholes (pōrt'hōlz') : openings in the sides of a ship

quill (kwĭl) : stiff feather once used as a pen for writing

rigging (rĭg'ĭng) : ropes supporting the masts of a sailing ship or used to set its sails

squire (skwīr) : country gentleman or landowner, local judge

staves (stāvz) : narrow strips of wood used in making wooden brackets and barrels

subject (sŭb jĕkt') : bring under control

tankard (tănk'ẽrd) : tall drinking vessel with a handle and lid, usually made of pewter

turnpike (tûrn'pīk') : toll road

tutor (tū'tẽr) : teacher who assists someone in a subject or course

wharf (hwôrf) : pier, structure beside a harbor where ships are loaded and unloaded

4470